Where The Lilacs Bloom Once Again

(Friddie Stoleru, 1954)

Roni Rosenthal

Where the Lilacs Bloom Once Again

Published by StoryTime World publishing house

https://www.facebook.com/FriddieStoleru
@RoniRosenthal
Roni-Rosenthal

Library of Congress Control Number: 2022911056
ISBN 13: 978-0-9792-8008-5 (paperback)
ISBN 13: 978-0-9792-8009-2 (ebook)

This book is dedicated to powerful women like Rosa and Friddie, and to my dad, who inspired me to write their story.

Family photo

In the front: Friddie (at the age of 4)
On the left side: Elvira and Isaac Stoleru
On the right side: Aurel and Aurica Rosenthal
Piatra Neamţ, 1923

In the front: Friddie (at the age of 4)
From left to right: Aurica, Aurel, Gisela, Elvira, Victor, Isaac
Piatra Neamț, 1923

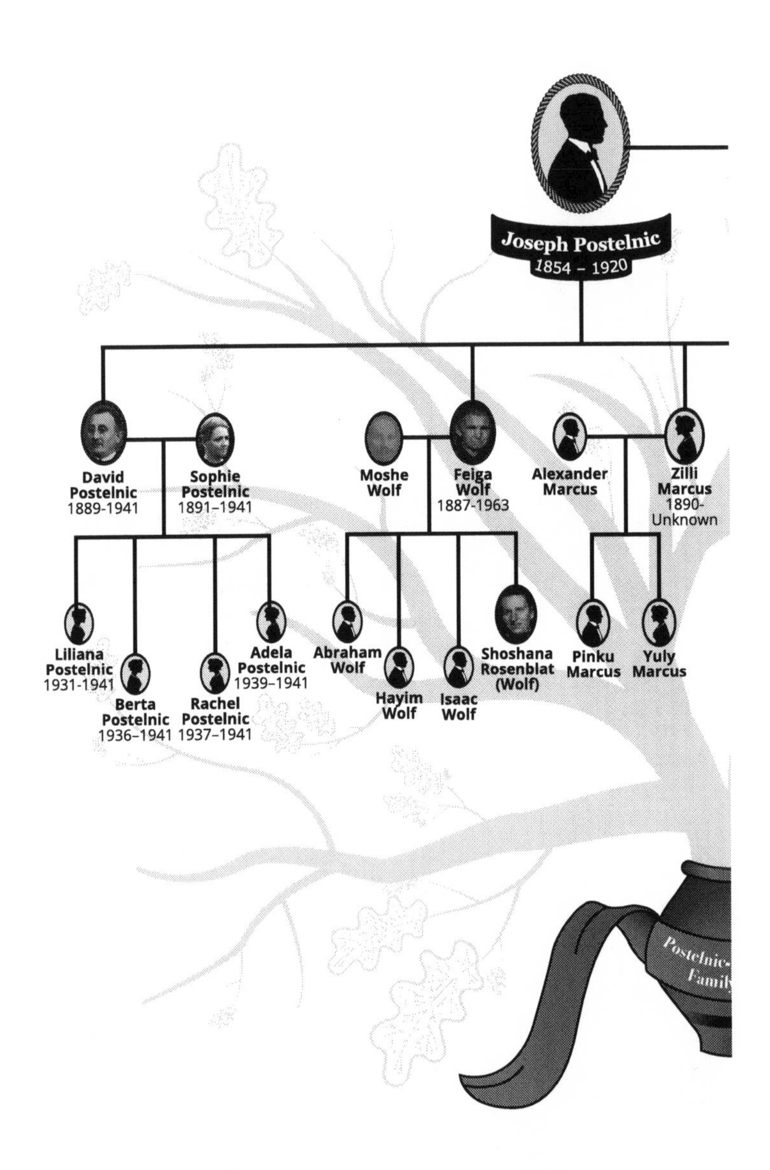
Joseph Postelnic
1854 - 1920
David Postelnic
1889-1941
Sophie Postelnic
1891–1941
Moshe Wolf
Feiga Wolf
1887-1963
Alexander Marcus
Zilli Marcus
1890-Unknown
Liliana Postelnic
1931-1941
Berta Postelnic
1936–1941
Rachel Postelnic
1937–1941
Adela Postelnic
1939–1941
Abraham Wolf
Hayim Wolf
Isaac Wolf
Shoshana Rosenblat (Wolf)
Pinku Marcus
Yuly Marcus

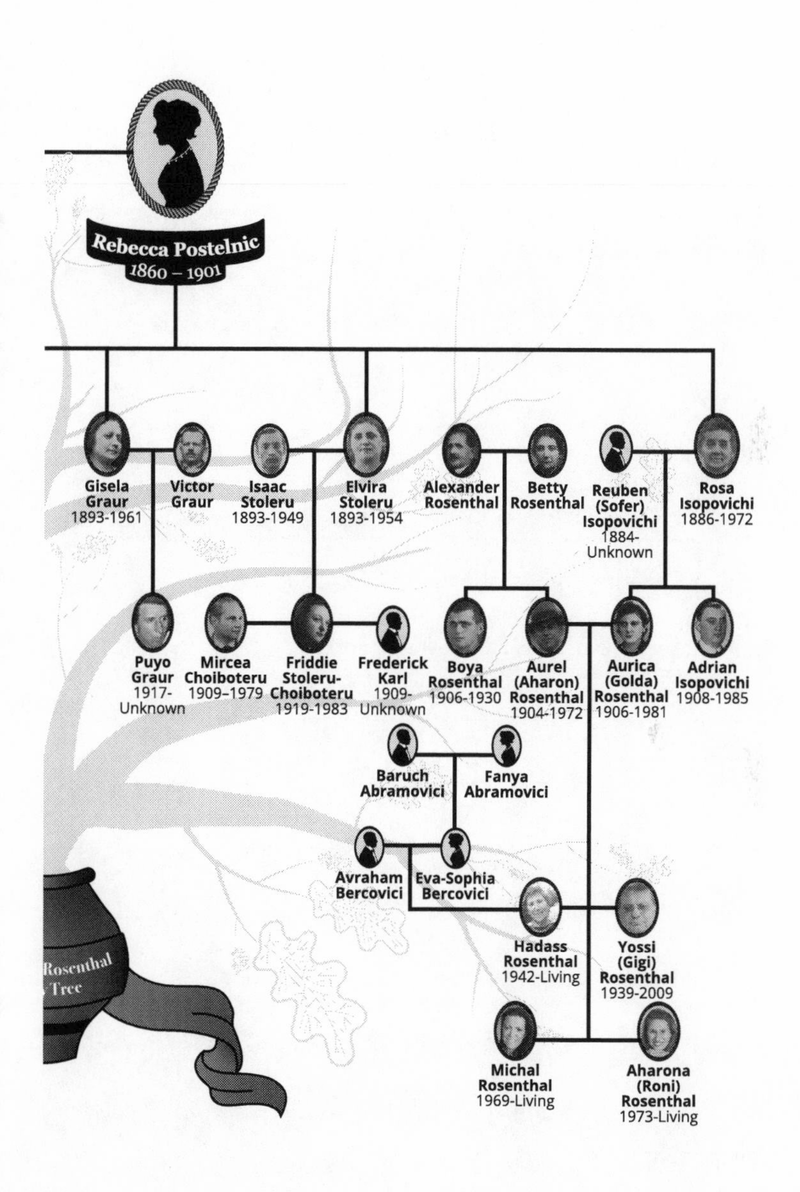
Rebecca Postelnic
1860 – 1901
Gisela Graur 1893-1961
Victor Graur
Isaac Stoleru 1893-1949
Elvira Stoleru 1893-1954
Alexander Rosenthal
Betty Rosenthal
Reuben (Sofer) Isopovichi 1884-Unknown
Rosa Isopovichi 1886-1972
Puyo Graur 1917-Unknown
Mircea Choiboteru 1909–1979
Friddie Stoleru-Choiboteru 1919-1983
Frederick Karl 1909-Unknown
Boya Rosenthal 1906-1930
Aurel (Aharon) Rosenthal 1904-1972
Aurica (Golda) Rosenthal 1906-1981
Adrian Isopovichi 1908-1985
Baruch Abramovici
Fanya Abramovici
Avraham Bercovici
Eva-Sophia Bercovici
Hadass Rosenthal 1942-Living
Yossi (Gigi) Rosenthal 1939-2009
Michal Rosenthal 1969-Living
Aharona (Roni) Rosenthal 1973-Living
Rosenthal
Tree

Table of Contents

Timelines

Postelnic-Rosenthal Family - Personal Events

Year	Event
1886	Rosa (Postelnic) Isopovichi is born
1887	Feiga (Postelnic) Wolf is born
1889	David Postelnic is born
1890	Zilli (Postelnic) Marcus is born
1893	The twins: Gisela (Postelnic) Graur and Elvira (Postelnic) Stoleru are born
1901	Rebecca Postelnic passes away
1901	David is attacked by bullies
1904	Rosa's wedding with Reuben Sofer-Isopovichi
1904	Aurel Rosenthal is born
1905	Feiga's wedding to Moshe Wolf
1906	Aurica (Isopovichi) Rosenthal is born
1908	Adrian Isopovichi is born
1909	Mircea Choiboteru is born
1911	Zilli's wedding to Alexander Marcus
1912	Elvira's and Gisela's weddings to Isaac and Victor
1918	David and Sophie's wedding
1919	Friddie Stoleru is born
1920	Joseph Postelnic passes away
1930	Aurica and Aurel Rosenthal's wedding
1934	Aurica and Aurel build their house in Bucharest
1937	Friddie's wedding to Nelu

1938	Friddie meets Freddy
1939	Yossi Rosenthal is born
1940	Friddie and Freddy get married
1940	Baruch Abramovici is arrested for the first time by the Legionnaires
1941	Friddie's interrogations; prison time begins
1945	Baruch and Fanya Abramovici leave for Israel
1947	Dr. Choiboteru passes away
1949	Isaac Stoleru passes away
1950	Friddie and Mircea fall in love
1951	The Rosenthal family leave for Israel
1951	Eva-Sophia and her family leave for Israel
1953	Mircea Choiboteru is released from labor camp
1953	Friddie is released from labor camp
1953	The Rosenthals buy their first home in Haifa, Israel
1954	Elvira passes away
1954	Friddie and Mircea's wedding
1961	Gisela passes away
1961	Friddie and Mircea hire a private detective
1972	Rosa Isopovichi passes away
1972	Aurel Rosenthal passes away
1979	Mircea passes away
1983	Friddie passes away

Major Events in the History of Romania between 1903-1950s (related to this book)

1903	First Pogrom (massacre) in Piatra Neamț
1914-1918	WWI—Romania joins forces in 1916 in favor of the Allies

1914	King Carol I dies and is succeeded by his nephew, King Ferdinand I (1914-1927)
1921	Prince Mihai is born
1927	Prince Mihai becomes king for the first time
1930	Prince Carol II, Ferdinand's I son, becomes king of Romania and establishes royal dictatorship
1939-1945	World War II
1940	King Carol II is forced to abdicate and leaves Romania
1940	Prince Mihai becomes king for the second time
1941 (Jan.)	Bucharest Pogrom (massacre)
1941 (June)	Iaşi Pogrom (massacre)
1944	King Mihai arrests Marshall Ion Antonescu; Romania reenters war on the Allies' side
1947	King Mihai is forced to abdicate; Communist-dominated government installed
1949	Danube Canal excavation project begins
1953	Joseph Stalin dies
1953	Danube Canal excavation project ends

***

1967	Nicolae Ceauşescu becomes president and general secretary of the Romanian Communist Party
1989	Protests against the communist dictator Nicolae Ceauşescu and his cabinet; the Ceauşescus are executed
1990	First free democratic elections in Romania since WWII

A disclaimer

The stories in this book are based on actual events, real people, and their experiences. In certain cases, the dialogues, timelines, and environmental descriptions have been changed for dramatic purposes. Some parts have been embellished or compressed for readability.

My family experienced and lived through the moments in this book. All I aim to do is to be their voice and tell their stories with honesty and compassion.

-- The Author

Prologue

Dad,

It's been twelve years since you left us. It's still so painful. Not a moment goes by that I don't think of you, remember your loving and powerful brown eyes, and wish to feel your familiar embrace again.

I write, I hurt, I cry. I know that tears and pain will accompany this book, as they have been an inseparable part of our family's history.

"Promise me," you said, "that our family's stories should not be hidden any longer. Their voices must be heard."

I, your faithful daughter, have listened. I vowed to write. I made the commitment to tell.

I will never forget the last time we sat together at the local Panera coffee shop in Rockville, Maryland. It was a bright, sunny day, in June 2009. I was a young mother, and you had just turned 70.

"Daddy," I said, "tell me Friddie's story again."

And you did.

I keep the cassette with the sound of your voice in my top drawer. I keep the notebook with your original drawing of our family tree in my jewelry box, now wrinkled with lines of folding and unfolding.

The warm rays of the sun caressed us. We talked about life in America and in Israel and, once again, you told me "The story of our family," as you called it. "The story of Friddie," you said, with sorrowful eyes. As with so many final moments, who knew it would be the last time I would hear it from you?

Do you remember when you took me on a trip to Romania in 1998, a few months before my wedding? We wandered through the streets of Bucharest, breathing in the smell of sweet garlic and listening to the mingling of car horns and gossiping mothers. On our walk, you first revealed the "secrets" to me.

I didn't say anything back then, because I didn't want to spoil the moment, but Mom told Miki and me the family stories years ago. She wanted us to appreciate the simple life and find joy in the small things around us. That time, in Romania, when I heard it from you firsthand, I was in awe.

You brought me to your childhood house on Georghe Manea Street in Bucharest. It was a simple, single-family home, surrounded by a high brick wall, the roof like a pointy red hat sitting contentedly on top. The pink roses blooming in the garden filled my nose with a sweet aroma, intertwining with the smell of baking apples and cinnamon from inside. So simple and yet—I could see nostalgia in the creases on your face. We stood there, watching the mother pull a *plăcintă cu mere*[1] from the oven and, for the only time in my life, I saw you shed a tear.

Did you remember your childhood? Did you feel a sense of longing for your parents, the same stinging pain I feel for you now?

I will not burden you with more words. I promised to write, and so I write. I promised to tell our story to the world, and so I will.

Your memory accompanied me along this entire journey. I hope you are proud of the result.

I miss you.

Your daughter,

Roni

1 Apple pie.

CHAPTER ONE

Friddie, 1937, Bucharest

Friddie stared outside her window, overlooking Cişmigiu Gardens. The lilacs and peonies flashed their wonderful display of purple and pink across the grounds, and families strolled across the pathways, fingers stroking the delicate petals. Friddie adored the view of the flowers, though she no longer went there to feel the smooth petals between her fingertips, as she had when she was a child. She had just turned eighteen the week before and was still living in her parents' modest two-bedroom apartment, in the heart of Bucharest.

Friddie brushed her charcoal-black hair, trying to straighten out her impossible curls. The city bustled with life: merchants loading their goods, black cars and horse-drawn carriages speeding down the roads, fruit sellers balancing two baskets with a long wooden pole draped across their shoulders. The laughter of happy shoppers chatting in the middle of the street floated up to her ears, even though she was on the third floor. Friddie smiled.

A little hat shop was right underneath her window. When she was young, she enjoyed watching the men who frequented the store. By their dress and manner of walking, she would imagine who they were, and which hat they were about to purchase. A skinny man with slender shoulders was obviously a bookkeeper, likely married to a squat woman with a broad physique, who made her husband's life miserable upon his return from work. Such a person, according to Friddie's imagination, would buy a tall hat, to give him some protection. She would tell her mother her tales of the men in the little hat shop, their laughter ricocheting around the kitchen.

Sometimes, handsome men visited the store. Their faces were clean-shaven, no beard or mustache, their hair short and modern. They reminded Friddie of those hardworking traveling businessmen, the ones she would read about in French magazines. She would rest her chin on the windowsill, close her eyes, and dream of her prince, who would one day carry her far away to mysterious and distant lands.

While Friddie enjoyed Bucharest, it lacked that ancient feeling of other cities, like Paris. Her parents had told her of the Great Fire of Bucharest that in March 1847 had destroyed a third of the city. The Romanian government invited French and Swiss architects to rebuild the city. They designed the new city according to the eclectic architectural style of Parisian architectural motifs. By the 1920s, many called Bucharest "Little Paris," or "the Paris of the East." Nevertheless, Friddie dreamed of its Western cousin.

From a young age, Friddie and her parents would walk the streets of Bucharest to admire its architecture. They would walk through the city's famous Arcul de Triumf, which stood in the city's main square, as a symbol of Romanian freedom from the Ottoman Empire. They would shop on the city's main street, Calea Victoriei, and explore the bustling boutique boulevard that resembled the Champs Elysees in Paris. Friddie would gawk at visitors from all over Europe, who came to shop on the famous street.

After World War I, the cultural and artistic life of the city flourished. Friddie could not wait to be old enough to experience it. Édith Piaf's French chansons flooded the streets, amusing club critics. Romanian theaters were in full swing, the Athenaeum concert hall hosted classical and jazz concerts. Huge ballrooms were flooded with hundreds of swing dancers doing the Charleston, Foxtrot, and Lindy Hop. Charlie Chaplin's silent movies were beginning to make room for 'talkie' feature films like *The Gold Diggers* and *The Jazz Singer*. Musicals were performed in theaters. The film *Dracula* was released and brought in curious visitors, seeking to find the lord of death. Residents frequented the stylish chic cafes, department stores, and lovely little shops, selling everything their hearts might desire. Modern cafeterias and authentic German, French, and American restaurants offered international cuisine.

Well-known fashion designers like Coco Chanel, Jeanne Lanvin, and Elsa Schiaparelli flooded the city in a wave. As Friddie visited the shops, she admired the Romanian women walking through the streets in the best of modern Parisian attire. Thin, bold, with sensual dresses up to the knees, revealing previously hidden legs. Short hair, cut to the jawline, highlighted their youth, recklessness, and thrills. Makeup and cosmetics became popular overnight.

The image of the 'new woman' blossomed. This woman was free and happy. She danced, she drank, she smoked. She took risks, she was independent and had the right to vote in local elections. Single women were offered employment opportunities as secretaries or schoolteachers. While Friddie yearned for this freedom, she lacked the desire for a job. And since she did not want to work, she knew she was to take a different path.

"Fridda!" Her mother's voice rose beyond the locked door. "Come on, Friddie, we're late. We must leave now for the hall."

Friddie ignored the increasingly frantic voice and continued to brush her hair.

Her wedding dress rested on the back of the chair, dangling from its hanger. The opalescent silk dress was embroidered with beads and lace sleeves, designed by her mother and tailored to fit Friddie's body by her talented aunts. As the brush moved through her now knotless hair, she took a tally of everything her parents had sacrificed for her to have this wedding. The wedding dress, so meticulously made. The wedding venue at the Magnificent Hall, which had cost her father a fortune to rent. The symphony orchestra, famous throughout Europe, hired to play through her vows.

Friddie closed her eyes and tried to imagine which of the guests had already arrived at the ballroom. Her *Tante*[2] probably were the first to arrive. Tanti Gisela, her mom's twin sister, was likely wearing a luxurious dress adorned with jewels, with a fur stole covering her shoulders. *Unchi*[3] Victor would be right beside her, dressed in a tailored suit. Their mischievous son, Puyo, had probably already checked out all the ladies in the hall and offered each one a taste of the best of champagne. Friddie smiled. After countless attempts by Tanti Gisela to conceive (which almost ended her life), Victor finally agreed to adopt a chubby ten-year-old boy from the orphanage. As they were leaving the orphanage, the boy started crying for his cat. When they discovered the hairless beast, they were initially repulsed by its smell, but took it home anyway. About a week later, the cat ran away. To their relief, Puyo did not.

Tanti Zilli, Unchi Alexander, and their two children, Pinku and Yuly, had already arrived from their home in Constanța the day before yesterday. They were staying at one of the most luxurious and comfortable *Athenee* Palace hotels. Her Tanti Feiga and her second husband, Nicolai, had come all the way from the northern town of Piatra Neamț to attend Friddie's wedding. Unchi David and his beautiful wife, Sophie, lived in Iași with their four adopted daughters, but were unable to come to Friddie's wedding. She re-read

---

2 Tanti in Romanian means aunt. Tante is plural for aunts.

3 Unchi in Romanian means uncle.

the telegram they had sent with their best wishes for her and her fiancé. Her fingers danced across the edges of the paper, wishing she too could be in Iași now, instead of here.

Friddie's favorite aunt, Tanti Rosa, lived in Bucharest and had been helping Friddie along every step of her wedding planning. Rosa was a talented, independent woman with bright red hair. Her husband vanished, assumed dead, at an early age. She always knew exactly what she wanted and how to get it.

Tanti Rosa came to Bucharest with her children, Aurica and Adrian, to be close to the rest of her family. At first, she ran a small business, sewing and repairing women's garments, out of their miniscule basement apartment. After a few years, Rosa realized that the delightful aroma from her stews and pastries not only enticed her children, and some curious street cats, but also curious snooping neighbors, who could easily become potential customers. Rosa had always loved cooking for her family and others, but only then realized she could support her children with her culinary talents. She opened the first catering business in Bucharest, and soon was overwhelmed with customers.

"Fridda!" Her mother's threatening voice boomed through the closed doors. Friddie continued to ignore the increasingly concerned voices outside and carried on brushing her hair. Her thoughts wandered once again, this time to her favorite teacher.

"If only Mademoiselle Charlotte was here now," Friddie whispered, in between brushes.

Mademoiselle Charlotte was the only teacher at Friddie's private French school whom she respected. Many teachers were deceived by Friddie's angelic face, fair complexion, flowing black curls, and innocent green eyes. Even her humble and naive parents were often tricked by her charms.

Despite the difficult financial situation of Friddie's parents, who ran a textile shop on Lipscan Street and earned a nice but not spectacular income, they insisted on giving their only daughter the best education. As soon as Friddie was old enough, they enrolled her in a private French school for girls.

Friddie despised it. But she soon realized that being stubborn and endearing could get her what she wanted. Cakes replaced the vegetable portion at lunch, skirts and school clothes were cut about ten inches above the knee at her request, and piano lessons were stopped even before they began. After many months of neglected homework, her parents hired private tutors to come to her house. Instead of learning, she charmed them to do her homework for her.

Mademoiselle Charlotte was not fooled by her, though. Friddie giggled as she remembered the worst scolding she had received.

She had cried, "I really didn't mean it, Mademoiselle Charlotte. I am so sorry. The scissors just slipped for a second from my hands, while I was busy solving the math equations on the board, and some of Madame Tublero's hair was cut while she closed her eyes. Will you find it in your heart to forgive me?"

The fiery eyes of her beloved teacher left no room for doubt. She knew the truth and punished Friddie accordingly.

Though harsh, Mademoiselle Charlotte was the only teacher who truly believed her students could control their own future. "You will find the answer within yourself," she used to say. "Only you know what's good for you. Only you can make it happen. I believe in you."

Another knock pounded on the door. Her father's voice broke through, gently urging her to leave her room. Friddie finally put the brush on the windowsill. Her hair was flawless and silky, much like the wedding dress, haunting her from across the room. She sighed, watching women with their children walking through the Gardens. She wished to be far away, roaming the streets, like she used to when she was younger.

Even before Friddie turned sixteen, rumors circulated about her scandalous behavior. Friddie was often seen far from her fancy school, walking around shops, while holding a cigarette between her arching fingers. Friddie would wear makeup and engage in flirtatious behavior with men older than her by at least a decade.

No, this was not acceptable behavior for a modest Jewish girl, raised in a proper home. The rumors occasionally reached her parents, who would deny them offhand. Even when they deigned to ask her about them, they would cave in front of her blameless face and sparkling eyes.

Friddie was a professional when it came to putting on a show. She never forgot the small details of her numerous lies.

There were many nights when Friddie would ask, "Mom, Dad, is it okay if I go to my good friend Elouise's house? We have so much homework to do, and we do not want to disturb your rest."

Then, she would take her friend's arm and, together, they would leave the apartment, dressed in the school's official uniform. A few minutes later, they would find a hiding place under the stairwell and change their school clothes into evening dresses they had hidden ahead of time. From there, they would rush to the ballroom, practicing their moves in the alleyways.

Few men escaped Friddie's remorseful bite. Her charming looks and rolling laughter left many aching hearts bleeding. She often ran into complications with jealous girlfriends, but all were convinced of Friddie's innocence in the whole situation, blaming the man instead. Friddie's confidence led her through life as if the universe were solely hers.

Her wrists were constantly doused with Eau de Parfum, emitting a lily, orange, and vanilla aroma. She wore fancy black-feathered hats, and her neck was decorated with white-golden necklaces, matching pearl earrings dangling from her ears. She often visited the most expensive fashion stores, treating herself to a new shiny hat or pair of leather shoes, while leaving the check under the name of one lover or another. Finally, she was a free Romanian woman. And she did not even have to work for it!

The one who unintentionally jeopardized Friddie's life of pleasure was her cousin, Puyo. When he turned seventeen, he began to frequent the same dance halls as her. His friends, who were mesmerized by the mysterious beautiful young woman, asked, requested, demanded, and even begged Puyo to make an official introduction. He refused, carefully watching to try to make sure his cousin never got into trouble, which she often did.

One evening, Puyo was arguing with his mother about spending too much time in the clubs.

In a rush of anger, he shouted, "Why can Friddie go out at night and drink champagne with all these different characters, and I am forbidden to have fun? Is that fair?"

His mother's reaction made him quickly realize he had betrayed his cousin. Unfortunately, he had no time to warn her of his mishap.

Gisela hurried to her sister the next morning. Elvira tried to deny the rumor at first, saying it was impossible. But she realized she should believe her twin, and talk to her husband, Isaac. That night, when Friddie tried to leave again, her parents stopped her at the door.

Friddie was too smart to deny it. She cried on her father's shoulders and said, "True, this is all true, but am I doomed to live such an unfulfilled life? If I cannot enjoy my youth now when I am still young and pretty, when can I? When the time comes, I promise you, I will marry a man you will approve of."

And Friddie kept her promise. The day after she turned eighteen, she showed up at her parents' house and introduced them to Nelu. Nelu was a quiet and dignified man, a professional accountant, who grew up in a decent Jewish home and was no doubt in love with Friddie. With sparkling eyes, he told the story of how they first met in a coffee house. He promised her parents he would take care of Friddie as if she were a precious rose, support her with his endless love, and see to all her needs. He also promised that Friddie would never have to work a day in her life, which suited her. Her parents gave their blessing, and the couple's engagement took place a few weeks later.

For a while, Friddie was happy. Nelu bought her gifts and took her to Bucharest's best and most famous restaurants. They would go to the theater, walk through the Gardens, and go out dancing most nights. Even though Nelu kept working as much as before he had met Friddie, he would always hurry home to his small apartment on Calomfirescu Street, only to leave just as quickly, to spend the evenings with his fiancée.

For a while, Friddie enjoyed his courtship. She would introduce her fiancé to her ex-lovers and friends, who appeared amazed at her choice. However, before three months had passed, Friddie felt boredom creeping into her heart. She missed dancing with strangers, wearing revealing evening gowns, spending the night in the arms of different men. Most of all, she missed having the affection of more than one lover.

Despite her growing boredom, both of their families pressured her to set a date for the wedding. Nelu would look at her pleadingly, though he would never force her to do anything. Friddie tried to dodge.

"I'm still too young. I still don't feel mature enough for a married life, nor bearing children."

"All my sisters and I got married at the age of eighteen," Elvira said. "Having children is a blessing and a mitzvah given to us by the Torah."

After several weeks, Friddie surrendered. They set a date for the wedding. Friddie hoped her feelings would change.

The wedding day had now arrived, but the dread had never left her chest. Her only solace was brushing her black curls, which she began doing again through the increasingly hysterical shouts outside. Her guests were waiting in the ballroom. The orchestra had been playing for an hour. The food was ready, and so was the rabbi. Her parents asked, begged, pleaded.

"Please, Friddie, think about the family, think about our guests."

At one point, she heard Nelu's voice, begging her to come out. "I'll be by your side," he whispered, "I'm very excited too."

Friddie brushed her hair, staring out the window. The white wedding dress still hung quietly on the back of the chair. Friddie could not find within her the inspiration needed to wear the dress, to wear the jewelry, to put on makeup, to perfume herself. Most of all, no one in the world could convince her to wear the doting smile required of a loving bride.

Mademoiselle Charlotte's voice echoed in her mind. "Only ***you*** know what's good for you. Only ***you*** can make it happen. I believe in you."

CHAPTER TWO

Rosa, 1901, Piatra Neamț

Piatra Neamț, a town in the province of Moldova in northeastern Romania, nestled at the foot of the Bistrița River. Blue skies and cotton candy clouds that do not forget to worship the sun expanded above the town. A picturesque and peaceful place, where calm and quiet reign. For many years, it seemed as if time stood still there.

The streets in Piatra Neamț were small and paved with stones. The walkways were adorned with flowers and evergreen climbers. The plants spoke of an era before human hands had ever interfered, nature ruling all spaces and moments. Even the horses pulling heavy carriages remained quiet, their hooves dancing lightly over the gravel, seemingly fearful of disturbing the birdsong.

Sitting outside my home, I used to thumb through my family's old album. The pages looked as if they were copied from faded pictures in a Van Gogh painting. Women strolled past, dressed in wide muslin dresses, and men in festive tuxedos, high hats, or wide-brimmed straw hats. Alongside cheerful carriages and workshops, we lived peacefully, side by side. Rich and poor, women and men, young and old.

There, in this European gem, my family began. Although my siblings and I have left our hometown, and our parents are no longer alive, Piatra Neamţ will forever remain home in our hearts.

I was born in 1886 to Joseph and Rebecca Postelnic, who gave me the name Rosa, for the beautiful flowers blooming in our garden. I was the oldest of five sisters and one brother. My parents lived in a modest house, located at the foot of a hill on the edge of town. I was born in that house, as were my siblings. In our backyard, we raised chickens for fresh eggs, and cows and goats for milk. In the front yard of the house, we planted a small vegetable garden that provided fresh onions, potatoes, eggplant, garlic, and basil for our family. We cut down trees in the woods during the summer months to heat the house in the winter.

My brother David lived in the attic, while my four sisters and I shared one bedroom.

Tata[4] was an honest and decent man, devoutly Jewish, with fiery brown eyes and a long beard, in which age had already left its mark. Mama was delicate and fragile. She worked day and night in the kitchen, beads of sweat running down her forehead as she cooked, cleaned, washed clothes, and did all the other chores that piled up in a house of six children. We were all by her side and helped Mama to the best of our ability.

Mama wore simple sky-blue dresses, whose color faded after many washes. Her brown hair was usually covered with a handkerchief, stitched from her old dresses. Her only decoration was the wedding ring Tata had given her. It was silver with a small, purple gem in the center. Like Tata, Mama came from an observant Jewish household, and although she prayed for good health morning and

4 Tata means dad in Romanian. Mama means mom.

evening, her prayers were never answered. Weakness and exhaustion would frequently overwhelm her, and she needed to rest often to regain her strength.

Summers were spent on the shores of the Bistrița River, splashing in the blue water and soaking up the bright sun. The *Domnitor*[5] of Romania, Alexandru Ioan Cuza, had built his wife a castle in Piatra Neamț. His wife, Elena Rosetti, and children would often come to spend the warm months here, enjoying the weather and cool river.

My siblings and I also used to scramble down to the shoreline of the Bistrița River to play. From a distance, we would see *Doamnă's*[6] entourage gathering for a boat ride. Our parents warned us not to disturb the Doamnă's rest, but we were curious to see what she was doing. As we'd swim up to the boat, the Doamnă would laugh, splashing us with water and telling us fishes to settle down. The day Doamnă Elena Rosetti died, in 1909, the whole town mourned. My siblings all prayed for the Doamnă, unaware that the royal family's fate would one day intertwine with ours.

We returned home from the river, only when the sun finally left the sky. Even the winter, which covered everything in a white blanket, was bearable. My siblings and I loved to play in the snow, build snowmen, and sled across the frozen water with sleighs we had made from wooden sticks. We were protected from freezing winds by the mountains surrounding our little town.

Our house had a large basement that was cool in the summer and warm in the winter. Mama would keep big barrels of pickles, bags of potatoes, sacks of flour, and jams in glass jars down there. I will never forget the wonderful aroma of lemon while she cooked sour *Ciorbă de Perișoare*[7] soup, salted herring, and cream sauce

---

5 The ruler of Romania between 1862 and 1881.

6 In Romanian it means the first lady or Madam.

7 Romanian traditional sour soup with meatballs.

with an abundance of onion and garlic, which we would pour over *mămăligă*[8] and *sarmale*[9]. On special occasions, Mama would bake cherry cake and smother it in delicious sugary thick cream. Years later, these flavors would still be embedded in my tongue and inspire my own cooking.

Tata had a unique talent for storytelling. When he returned from his travels selling fabric, we would huddle at his feet by the fireplace and wait impatiently to hear a new story. He once told us the story about how we got our last name, Postelnic. He said that many years ago people did not have last names. People lived in isolated villages like ours, on distant farms, and if a telegram was sent or a guest arrived for a visit, it was clear to everyone who the message was for.

Over the years, however, the farms in the area multiplied and there were more than two people who had a similar first name. People began to invent last names for each other. Some people chose their family name according to the geographical area in which they lived, or according to a special gem or jewel which their name was associated with. Our forefathers preferred to choose a family name that reflected the family business. Thus, the name Postelnic was chosen. It means someone who was a senior administrator within the royal services. According to Tata, one of our forefathers served as the personal secretary of the kingdom.

Mama had a talent for sewing dresses and lace design. In her youth, before she fell ill and her strength faded, she would sit by the sewing machine with a dreamy look on her face. Tata would buy silk cloth and sewing threads to satisfy his wife's desires. Within a few hours, the fabric would turn into a spectacular dress. The dresses were donated to the local synagogue and given to women who typically couldn't afford them.

---

8 A traditional Romanian polenta made of boiled water, salt, and cornmeal.

9 Rolled cabbage.

Even after Mama's lung disease had ravaged her insides, she would sneak to her sewing machine. There, between stitches, she would spit blood into a white handkerchief. Early in the morning, Tata would find her trembling and pale as her new dresses. As he carried her in his arms back to bed, she would look at him with the same dreamy look, as if she were still creating another spectacular dress.

I was fifteen when Mama passed away. Since I was the oldest daughter, I was expected to take responsibility for the family's chores. My siblings were by my side and helped me.

Feiga was one year younger than me and a self-proclaimed Zionist. Although she no longer attended school, books were the love of her life. Once her chores were done, she would find a place under the thick oak tree in our backyard and read stories of returning to Jerusalem. Abraham Mapu's[10] fantastical stories pushed her imagination far to the Zionist state that would be established one day, while Hayim Nahman Bialik's[11] sweeping prose of pain and longing encouraged her to hope.

Zilli was fragile, just like our mother. She looked like a porcelain doll with golden hair and blue eyes that had a look of amazement, as if astounded by the beauty of the world. Her health worried us, especially after Mama died.

On the day she was born, the midwife whispered, "She might not survive the first night."

Suction cup treatments, stinging salt baths, and bitter-smelling ointments did not help. Zilli suffered from high fevers frequently, and red spots would spread all over her skin. The town doctor was a regular guest in our home.

---

10 A famous Hebrew novelist.

11 The famous Hebrew poet.

"She might be gone by dawn," he ruled one evening, his eyes glistening.

"She will survive!" exclaimed Gisela. "And live many years after you're gone!"

Her fiery eyes left no doubt. The determination in the voice of the eight-year-old girl aroused admiration among her family. David hugged his little sister and sat her on his lap.

"If you believe so, so do I," he said.

Elvira, who was born six minutes before her twin sister, Gisela, would refuse to stop working until all of the house chores were done. Every morning, she would tie her curly hair high on her head. Her green eyes would fill with determination, and while her lips whistled a war march, she would stand tall over the wooden board and barrels of boiling water, scrubbing, rubbing, and abusing the cloth, until not a single stain was left. Only at night did she allow herself to rest. Under the light of a dim candle, she would embroider her dreams into canvas, trying to dispel her anxious thoughts.

When Mama was still alive, we would visit the synagogue on Shabbat and the High Holidays. Mama would dress us in the Shabbat clothes she had made. When she got sick, I started dressing my younger siblings in festive clothes to continue the family tradition.

Rarely did Tata join our visits to the synagogue. Although he was an observant Jew, he did not believe in attending group prayers.

"God examines kidneys and heart," he claimed, "so even when I ask for something inside my mind, God listens to my wishes."

Though he rarely talked about it, Tata actually did not attend the synagogue because he opposed the separation of classes in our small town, especially at the synagogues. The merchant's synagogues, which our family was considered part of, were more affluent than the one that served artisans and peasants.

"We are all equal before God," Tata would say over and over again, but it fell on deaf ears.

The rich did not want to share their space with the poor, and the poor… Well, who would listen to them anyway? While affluent citizens were privileged to pray in the main hall of the Beit Midrash, the poor were expected to pray in a small space with unstable wooden benches and a terrible mildew smell.

After Mama's death, Tata mourned for a long time. He disappeared in his grief, stayed in his room and became isolated in his thoughts. Words of comfort were blocked by his sorrow. His hair turned white overnight and his thick beard grew thinner. We left trays of food in front of the doorway, which were often retrieved untouched. He abandoned his job as a fabric merchant. Sometimes, he mumbled incoherently. Among the few words he uttered were his wife's name and phrases from the Psalms.

At first, our financial situation was stable. The metal jug in the kitchen had enough *Lei*[12] that we could use at the farmers' market and butcher shop on the corner.

Quickly, however, the metal jug began to empty. David insisted on dropping out of school to support our family. He was twelve years old and felt responsible. Most of his friends had already dropped out, so he felt no regret.

He found work as a stable boy with a devout Christian family. His job was to clean the stables and feed the horses. Hours passed as he scraped the hay and collected it into piles. His "payments" were the wounds and warts that popped up all over his small body. Often, he would return home bleeding. I begged him to leave the job. I promised that the family would be fine, even without the meager coins he brought home. Nevertheless, David refused.

"This is my responsibility," he said, his fists clenched at his side as he would leave for the day.

12 The Romanian currency at the time.

One evening, on his way home, a mob of boys attacked him. They stole the coins he had received an hour earlier for his work in the stable. But they were not satisfied with that.

"Stinking Jew," they shouted at him, throwing him to the ground and beating him.

They kicked and broke his ribs and arms, aiming for his head. They broke his knees with a hammer and smashed his back with a barrel of oil. They left him there to die, while laughing and jeering. David lay still, unable to feel the blood flowing from his forehead. The neighbors found him, barely alive.

CHAPTER THREE

Friddie and Freddy, 1938, Bucharest

After refusing to get married, Friddie decided to take some time away from the city and the gossiping mothers with their sneering debutantes. Her Tanti Zilli offered to let her stay in their summer home in Eforie Nord, near the town of Constanța and the Black Sea.

Friddie spent her time sunbathing and strolling along the beach. She would walk for hours along the coarse sand, letting the blue waves engulf her feet. Some days she would draw infinite shapes in the golden sand, enjoying the caressing rays of the sun on her black hair.

In Eforie Nord, her mind was free. She imagined being carried away by a bird to distant places. She would soar far from the borders of Romania, from the clubs and parties that had been her home in recent years. Most importantly, away from the expectations of her parents, who had forced her to choose such a dull, predictable future.

About a week after Friddie's arrival at the summer house in Eforie Nord, while having dinner at La Vaca Sfântă, one of the city's most famous restaurants, a young man dressed in a suit approached her.

"Excuse me, Mademoiselle," he addressed her politely.

Friddie didn't look up, already bored. She knew what was about to come.

"I couldn't help but notice the scent of your perfume tonight," he said.

Friddie laughed. "Excuse me? That's the strangest compliment I have heard. Do you really think such a lousy line would get my attention?" She grinned, not lifting her eyes off the menu.

"I'm sorry." His voice was startled. "You see, my table is right over there… I'm a scientist, tasked with finding fragrances and perfumes." This piqued her interest, and she finally made eye contact. His hair was pitch black, and he was watching her with such intense brown eyes that she could not look away. "I am in charge of importing and exporting special scents for Romania. I would say that tonight you are adorned with a lilac scent. Am I right?"

"A lilac scent? Maybe, who knows?" She shrugged and felt her cheeks warm.

"You see, as a perfumer, I am in a constant search for new fragrances that will appeal to Romanian women. I have visited countless places inside Romania and around the world. Rare scent arouses my curiosity."

Friddie watched him, intrigued. His hair was carefully combed back, his suit tailored, he wore an expensive gold watch, and no wedding ring.

"*S'il vous plaît.*" She waved her hand at the vacant chair across from her. "Please sit down."

He motioned for the waiter to come over.

"May I order you a glass of wine?" His grin was wide.

Friddie ordered white Burgundy, and the man asked for a cold martini as he took his seat.

"I'm sorry, Mademoiselle. I forgot to introduce myself." He bowed his head. "My name is Frederick Karl." He watched her with those eyes, and she lost her breath. "And you are?"

Friddie's lips curled. "My name is Fridda, but please call me Friddie."

He smiled. "Everyone calls me Freddy."

Friddie could not take her eyes off the dimples in his cheeks when he smiled. His shiny black hair, broad shoulders, and button nose made Friddie's heart stagger. At the end of the evening, as he wrapped her in his arms while dancing, Friddie knew she would fall in love with this man.

Over the next few weeks, Friddie and Freddy spent every minute together. In the mornings, he joined her on her walks across the golden sand. She would let the wind mess up her hair, so Freddy's gentle fingers could remove sand from her curls, as well as taste the sea salt on her lips. At night, they went to clubs to dance, holding each other tightly, as if the next day, one of them might disappear.

Freddy and Friddie spent more and more time exploring each other. He would buy her exquisite jewelry and special perfumes, putting them on her milky white neck once she woke up, naked in his arms. Sometimes, he would return to his hotel room and attend to business, but he would soon return to her, sweeping her off to some dance hall. One morning, as she was waking up, she realized that he was gone. He had left a note that he had to meet some potential investors. As she wandered to go get breakfast, she saw him in a cafe, sitting with a couple of men in black suits. She thought nothing of it and went on her way, hungover and desperate for breakfast.

After nine weeks of sandy walks and stolen kisses, Friddie's vacation was about to end. She sobbed in his arms, begging him to come back to Bucharest with her. Freddy told her that he would try, but he would be traveling for a long time, in search of new perfumes. He told her he had scheduled several business meetings in various places in Europe, and he had to see if those opportunities would come to fruition. He held her as she cried, smoothing her hair and promising that they would be together soon.

The first light of sunrise peeked over the horizon, and Friddie buried her face in his chest, begging for God to turn time backwards. Waves from the Black Sea pressed against the shore, and she thought they sounded almost mournful. As if the world were sad for them to be apart.

"Will you come back to me?" asked Friddie, tears rolling down her cheeks.

"Of course, *mon amour.*" Freddy hugged her tightly, holding her close to his chest. He kissed her red lips once again and whispered words of love in her ears.

"Will you wait for me?" he asked.

"I will wait for you until the day I die," she swore.

#

The following weeks passed slowly. She returned to her parents' apartment and refused to go out or meet with her old friends. All her thoughts were devoted to her memories with Freddy, her longing for him. Her mother would leave food outside her door, and she would pick at it slowly, wishing she were eating it with her beloved.

One day, she received a letter from Freddy. Friddie hugged and kissed the envelope as if it were a delicate flower. Tears streamed down her cheeks. She opened the envelope with her fingers, unable to wait for a knife. The note read:

"My Friddie, the days pass by so fast. I travel from one place to another, searching for new aromas. Yesterday, I was in London, and today I am on my way to Paris! I'm meeting businessmen and scientists. We have discussed some interesting possibilities. Only at nights, I allow myself to ache and feel lonely. I can't stop thinking about you, about us. I long to hold you in my arms. *Te iubesc*[13], Freddy."

---

13 I love you in Romanian.

Six weeks passed slowly. She spent her days longing for more letters, but more so, longing for his touch.

When the day came at last, Friddie cried with joy. She rose at dawn with the sun, washed her face, put on her makeup and the lilac perfume that had become her favorite, and the bottle-green gown that accentuated the green in her eyes. This time, no one had to convince her to put on her smile.

Her heart seized every time a car stopped under her window. Men came to visit the little hat shop, but she did not notice them, much less make up stories about their lives. She stared out the window, her high-heeled shoes tapping on the carpet.

Friddie heard a car stopping next to her parents' apartment. "Freddy," she yelled as she rushed down the stairs. Her heart was beating so fast. It was him. It was her man.

The couple spent all their time together over the next couple of weeks. They mostly stayed in Freddy's apartment, cuddling and exploring each other's bodies until dawn. They sometimes left to go dancing, watch a play, or attend a concert at the theater.

One night, Freddy told her that he had tickets to the opera. She put on her best dress: a shiny black evening gown, embroidered with gems. As they walked home after the show, a cool breeze making the gems on her dress clink against each other, Freddy stopped her at the gate of the Gardens. He got on one knee and gave her a huge sparkling diamond ring, with matching earrings set with red and black gems. Tears welled up in her eyes and she fell onto him. He promised that this night was just the beginning.

A few weeks later, ignoring her parents' concerns, she moved into his spacious apartment in the La Sosea district, known for its elegant houses and well-known tenants. It was a luxurious building, the entrance adorned with two heavy statues of lions that greeted the visitors. Marble figurines adorned the foyer and lounge. In Freddy's apartment, impressionist murals by Claude Monet, Alfred Sisley, and

Berthe Morisot decorated the walls, creating a colorful but majestic atmosphere. The long panoramic windows were covered in green velvet curtains, the stair railing was wrapped in gold, and in each room hung a magnificent chandelier, adorned with gold bells.

Friddie felt as if her dream of living in a palace with her prince was finally coming true.

One morning, Friddie woke up feeling terribly nauseous. She rushed to the bathroom and vomited. After washing her face and calming down, she thought she must have eaten something spoiled the night before.

The next day, when the incident repeated itself, a concern rose in her heart. She said nothing, hoping her fears would go away. But a week later, she knew for sure. She feared Freddy's reaction, as he had never shown any particular interest in having children. Freddy was nine years older than Friddie, but it seemed that his life as a bachelor, exploring the world for the perfect perfume fragrance, suited him well.

Yet, the next morning, when Freddy asked, "What's wrong, my love? The greenish tint of your skin doesn't suit you. Maybe you should see a doctor?" Friddie burst into tears.

"I'm so sorry," she cried, "I don't know how it happened. I was so careful..."

At first, Freddy looked shocked. His face flushed immediately, and he froze, looking like one of the statues downstairs. After a moment, he regained his calm and pulled Friddie close to him. He kissed her head and neck, wiping her tears and whispering, "I'm so happy." He looked into her glistening eyes. "Will you allow me, my dear Friddie, to ask for your parents' blessing? There will be no happier person than me, if they say yes."

Her parents opposed their union.

"He's not for you," her mother said. "He's nine years older than you, Friddie. He's living his life as a bachelor."

"But I love him, Mom!" Friddie begged. "I love him so much."

"You hardly know him, and he is not even Jewish!"

"Mom, I don't want to live without him. I cannot. He is the one who really loves me, understands me. Please, Mom. Please try to understand..."

"My Friddie, my beloved daughter," Elvira hugged her. "Love will disappear one day and all you will have left is a huge hole in your heart and marriage to a man who travels the world, leaving you alone at home. What will happen to you, what will happen to your happiness? You need someone to be by your side. What good is a man who is used to living alone? What kind of life will your children have, with a father who is not here?"

Despite their concerns, the wedding took place at the town hall. Freddy had no relatives in Romania. His father had passed away when Freddy was very young, and his mother returned to Germany to be with her family. Freddy grew up in a boarding school and had no siblings as far as he knew. He rarely kept in touch with his mother in Germany. He insisted on a formal but modest ceremony. Once the ceremony was over, only members of Friddie's family and her close acquaintances were invited to celebrate at one of the better-known restaurants in town. Friddie's face glowed. She was happy at last. The pregnancy only added to her beauty. Freddy hugged his bride and kissed her belly, the fruit of their love.

After a few weeks of getting to know each other, Friddie's parents warmed up to their new son-in-law. They learned to like Freddy, though they were unhappy about the circumstances of the marriage. They learned to appreciate his wit and the love he showed toward their daughter. Elvira and Isaac knew that they could never let anything cause a rift between them and their only daughter's happiness, ignoring their growing sense of dread as the birth approached.

The night after her nuptials, Friddie closed her eyes, finally able to let her mind rest. Her dream of meeting her perfect prince had come true, and nothing could take away her happiness.

CHAPTER FOUR

Friddie, 1940, Bucharest

In the weeks after the wedding, Friddie quickly got used to her new status as Freddy's wife. The couple were central to Bucharest's vibrant social life, invitations flowing through their mailbox to events and opening nights. Friddie would go to the dance halls, once a symbol of her freedom, but this time proud to be there with her husband's arm around her waist. Friddie would accompany Freddy to his business meetings, where he would proudly introduce his new wife. Then he would dive into business, while Friddie would stare at the flowers outside, smiling at her good fortune.

By October 1939, cannons were thundering across the European continent. Life in Bucharest went on, the Romanian people relying on their routine to retain a sense of normalcy. The Postelnic family paid attention to the news, though, as did the other Jewish Romanians. European Jews were disappearing, and Romania's political security warned residents to stay alert. Headlines in the newspaper shouted, "Save Romania" and "Romania is no longer Great."

Romania initially declared neutrality, having its own problems to deal with. But the Soviet Union was intent on conquering Romania, and by 1940, Romania had already lost many of its geographical territories. The region of Bessarabia was divided between Moldova and Ukraine; northern Transylvania was handed over to Hungary; and southern Dubrova was given away to the Bulgarian authorities. Germany invaded Poland, and the Polish heads of state fled and found a political safe haven in Romania. People began to criticize King Carol II for surrendering to dictators and not opposing the hostile takeover of their land. They called for a change in regime. The king was exiled and replaced by his youngest son, Prince Mihai. The very same day that King Carol II boarded the train with his mistress and hurried off to Portugal, Friddie went into labor.

Friddie was in the kitchen peeling potatoes, her belly swollen to the point it touched the countertop. Every movement felt heavy, and her back ached when she walked or stood. She could not find comfort in any position. Yet, she revelled in the joy that her child would be joining them soon. She only hoped that Freddy would return from his journey and be by her side during the birth.

Three weeks earlier, Freddy had left on an impromptu business trip. He kissed his wife and promised to return soon. Then he stepped into a taxi and sped off. Before he left, he talked about how much pressure he was under to find the right partners for his fragrance business, especially with multiple wars breathing down their necks and Romania's economic and political structure in shambles. He did not tell her where he was looking for new partners, and she did not feel like she needed to know. Until now.

Before setting off, Freddy hugged his wife and warmly stroked her belly. "Will you wait for me?" he asked.

Friddie nodded, her eyes flooding with tears. She didn't like herself like that, weeping. She didn't want to be the damsel in distress, depending on a lover to run her life. She wanted to be like her Tanti Rosa, who ran a successful business by herself, while raising two children. Yet Freddy melted her in a way no one ever had before.

Every time he left her, she mourned his loss, even before he reached the door.

Freddy wiped the tears from her eyes gently. "You know I'll always take care of you, right?" He bent down and kissed her swollen belly.

Friddie nodded. She couldn't say a word through the tears choking her throat.

"Wait for me," he whispered to the unborn baby in her belly. "I'll be back soon." Freddy kissed his wife again and hurried off.

Now, in the kitchen, Friddie felt her stomach clench. A sudden gush of water soaked her bare feet. She immediately wished she knew where Freddy was or how to reach him. He had left her no information. She leaned against the counter and prayed. She prayed that he would hear her pleas and come back to her. After a moment of silence, she called her parents. They rushed to her apartment and drove her to the hospital.

The birth lasted nearly thirty hours. Friddie fainted from the pain, waking up for brief moments, just to lose consciousness again. When she was awake, she would writhe in pain, begging God to help her. To bring Freddy to her. The nurses in the maternity ward tried to calm her down, encourage her. They helped her regain consciousness and offered gentle words. The doctor examined her, but had no news. "The labor is going as planned," he said. "Each woman experiences this process differently. Patience, my dear, just be patient."

"Push," the midwives encouraged her. "Push as hard as you can."

Friddie screamed. She tried, she pushed, she rested, she pushed again. Pain was cutting her from the inside out, turning her gut over and burning her like hot coals.

"Freddy, where are you?" she sobbed. Friddie closed her eyes, trying to imagine his loving smile, caring eyes, his soft lips. Only these memories could get her through this pain. Only thoughts of him could give her hope.

The birth lasted a long time. The pain exhausted her. "God, please help me ..." Her lips formed the words again and again.

"It will be alright," the midwife promised. "Just a little more. Just keep pushing. You're doing great."

Suddenly there was silence. Darkness. "Oh, God!" the midwife's assistant shouted and fled the room. Sobbing filled the room. Friddie wasn't sure if she was the one crying. Darkness enveloped her.

In the distance, she heard the doctor's voice. He sat next to her and held her hand. "I'm sorry, Friddie. We tried the best we could. The baby did not survive. Sleep now, dear child. Get some rest."

CHAPTER FIVE

Rosa, 1903, Piatra Neamț

The Jewish community in Piatra Neamț played an important role in the development of the town, from textiles to agriculture, marketing of products to trading. Due to our strong role in the town, we were not subject to daily restrictions, as in other towns. We lived among the non-Jewish community and ran successful businesses. Our doctors were allowed to run their own practices.

But even though I enjoyed some freedom, I still grew up under the persecutions and restrictions of being Jewish.

Taxes were imposed on us, due to our being "members of the Abrahamic religion." The synagogues were granted building permits, but only on the condition that they be built of wood, to emphasize that they were temporary. The local Jewish society, Chevra Kadisha, was responsible for planning Jewish ritual ceremonies, as well as funeral arrangements, synagogue management, hospital visits, and other community needs. The town often arrested the leaders for no reason. Local school curriculums were reformed to be more patriotic. Courses on the national history of Romania became mandatory. Every morning, our students had to stand and salute the great leaders.

As I got older, the persecution of the Jewish community intensified. Anti-Semitism and blood libels increased. We were perceived as infidels, despised more than the Turks. We were not a small minority in the province of Piatra Neamţ, but we felt disdained and unwanted everywhere we went. By the late nineteenth century, we could no longer buy land, even if we could afford it. The town's public schools tried to prevent Jewish children from enrolling, and a large sign hung above the town's hospital that read, "No entry for Jews."

"The killers of Jesus should be killed," was often graffitied on the houses of Jews in town.

One hot evening in 1903, I was telling a story to my siblings about golems, fanning myself with one of Feiga's pamphlets. Suddenly, we heard loud voices rising in the street. As the voices got closer, I put out the candles and rushed my siblings into the basement. Tata burst out from his room, fear etched in his eyes. We hid behind large wooden crates, jammed between the jars of cabbage and sacks of potatoes. We shivered, though it was not cold.

The noises did not calm down until the sun broke through the horizon, like our savior. We remained behind the crates, holding each other silently. Tata finally dared to leave when the basement was totally filled with light from outside. We remained still, and I began to sing to keep my siblings distracted.

When he finally returned, Tata's face was full of terror. He brought us upstairs and sat us around the cold fireplace. "All the Jewish businesses were destroyed," he said. "Leaflets are scattered all over the place, calling the shutdown of Jewish stores. Our Jewish community leaders Sol Drimmer and Aron Chelbert, among others, have been kidnapped. They're likely being tortured at the police station. The local chief of police has promised to release them for a large sum of money."

Tata put his head in his hands, and sat there, unmoving for hours. Eventually, he went back to his room, refusing to come out for days. I took some coins from the metal jug, practically empty, and brought the money to the synagogue. I wanted to help free our leaders.

The stores were renovated and reopened. Silence returned to the town, but hostility was felt everywhere. We did not always know how to distinguish foe from friend and felt like we were always waiting for the next pogrom.

#

After the attack on my brother David in 1901, he lay in bed, shouting out random words deliriously. When he wasn't writhing in pain, he was unconscious. His body temperature remained high for weeks, sweat staining the white sheets.

While Elvira, Feiga, and I took care of the housekeeping, Zilli and Gisela took care of David. They smeared his body with ointments they had received from the town doctor and placed damp cloths on his forehead to absorb some of his heat.

Tata spent a good amount of time by David's bed, praying. The evening the neighbors knocked on our door, letting us know they had found David lying on the street, lifeless, Tata burst into tears and pleaded with God. He tore at his clothes and shouted, "God, please help me. Do not take my only son away from me."

We carried David home and called the doctor. We laid him in bed and cleaned his wounds. All the while, Tata wept bitterly. "I was wrong, I have sinned, I was guilty... Forgive me, God, our Supreme Sovereign, Holy ruler of the universe," he cried.

David did not die that night. Slowly, his breathing returned to normal. He moaned in pain and anguish, but didn't give up. Most of the time, his mind was still vague, but sometimes he opened his eyes and looked around for a moment. When his eyes met Tata's, he would close them again, his face calm.

A few weeks after the incident, David started murmuring more coherently. "Mamă, Mamă." His lips moved softly. "Water," he whispered a few days later.

The town doctor was less optimistic. "There was likely a brain injury. His speech may be impaired, as well as his ability to walk. It will take a long time for him to recover. If he ever does."

#

Our financial situation was deteriorating. The neighbors occasionally brought hot food to the house, but that was all they could afford. Tata tried to return to his previous occupation as a fabric merchant, but without success. Customers left him in favor of other traders.

With great sorrow, we had to sell Mama's Shabbat dresses. The affluent neighbors of the town hurried to purchase them. Each dress was a work of art in itself and had cost Mama hours of hard work. These were white cloth dresses, embroidered with red threads and golden linen ribbons, in Romanian tradition. Mama made sure to add her own unique embroidery to each dress. On one dress, she embroidered a roaring lion. On another, a white dove protected the garment. As I sold her last dress, my fingers traced the embroidery, memorizing the patterns.

Because of our difficult situation, we were now considered to have the same status as the artisans and peasants. When we finally went back to the synagogue, a few weeks after Mama passed, we were sent to huddle on the small wooden benches at the back of the synagogue. Some neighbors compassionately accompanied us.

It was our first and last visit to the Great Synagogue after Mama's death. I felt so embarrassed that I swore never to step inside again.

Every Sunday, in the early morning hours, the town hosted a farmers' market. Horses, traders, and customers crowded into the square next to the Church and the bell tower, named after Great

Stephen. There, merchants would sell their wares, shouting to the crowd. People would gather around the carts carrying agricultural and wholesale produce, such as milk, cheeses, fabrics, goats, chickens, fruits, and vegetables. The market was full of color and aromas, the perfume of flowers mixing strangely with souring milk.

When we were young, we would accompany our parents to the market. For us, it was a real celebration. We loved walking around the carts, petting young goats, tasting *papanashi*[14], and choosing a tiny piece of cloth to make a new rag doll.

I remembered the feeling of silk scraps between my fingers as I helped my siblings pile our belongings into our cart. Books, white porcelain dolls, golden forks and knives that our parents received on their wedding day, sheets and bedding that Mama brought as a dowry from her parents' house, and the festive Shabbat utensils, all were heaved on top of hay and blankets. Tata cried as he placed Mama's silver wedding ring, with the small purple gem, in the cart.

Gisela whimpered when she saw all the family heirlooms lying in the cart. Zilli hurried to hug and comfort her sister. Elvira sighed and said, "I hope we can make enough to buy flour, dry cheese, potatoes, and sausage for the winter." I put my arm around Feiga, who was looking with teary eyes at the books of Zionism she had donated to the pile. Only Gordon's poems were kept. She held the saved book in her arms, like a nation embracing the Zionist dream.

I climbed on the cart and tied the objects down with a thick rope. I knew that any scratch could bring down their price and I dreaded having to argue and quarrel to sell them at a decent price. My fingers brushed against Mama's wedding ring, and I slipped it into my pocket. I would sell it at the end, I decided. It was hard for me to let go of the ring, Mama's last personal keepsake, the ring I had hoped to wear one day, when I found someone who loved me as much as Tata loved Mama. I might not have to sell it after all. There is always hope.

---

14 A traditional Romanian dessert, similar to a doughnut covered in sour cream and jam.

CHAPTER SIX

The Rosenthal Family, 1939, Bucharest

Yossi Rosenthal, or as everyone called him by his Romanian nickname, Gigi, was born in Bucharest in May 1939 to the happy parents, Aurica and Aurel, and his proud grandmother, Rosa. Rosa's daughter, Aurica, cooed over her baby, grateful to God to have blessed them with a boy, after six failed pregnancy attempts. Yossi was a beautiful and curious baby. As he grew, he carefully examined every corner of the modest house. His parents marveled at the cleverness of their son, who began crawling, sitting, standing, and reading ahead of time.

His parents had met at the Elena Rosetti fabric store on Strada Lipscan, where they both worked. Aurica left school the day after she turned fourteen, and Aurel, who had finished school, began working in the shop as a teenager to support his family.

Aurica and Aurel's wedding took place on a summer day in 1930, at the small city hall. Boya, Aurel's younger brother, was given a twenty-four-hour leave of absence from the military to attend the wedding. Their father, Alexander, was excited to see his two young sons finally back together. He hugged them and wiped away a tear of joy that escaped from his eyes. Alexander prayed for his late wife and hoped she would bless them today, from her place in heaven. The father kissed his son's cheeks and went to sit down. Boya slapped his brother on his back, and they hugged, trying to keep the tears from flowing. Aurel did not realize it would be the last time he saw his brother, who died a few weeks later, in a training accident.

On the day of her daughter Aurica's wedding with her beloved Aurel, Rosa wore a light blue dress, embroidered with gold threads, and a matching hat. She examined herself in the mirror several times. Sometimes, she wondered what her children's lives would have been like, if she had not moved to Bucharest, but stayed in their hometown, Piatra Neamţ. She never remarried after losing her husband, Reuben. Thoughts and doubts about him would occasionally come to mind. What exactly happened to him that day, when the horse kicked his head? Did he do something that made the horse upset? Did he know she came to see him with her brother, David? Where was he laid to rest? Why was his burial place unknown?

A chill ran through her spine, but Rosa managed to shake the dark thoughts from her mind. She put on a smile and fixed her hat. She glanced in the mirror. It was a time for celebration today. Soon, she would be among her family and friends. She had worked tirelessly, preparing the cuisine for this event, and everything looked perfect. She looked at the sky, hoping Reuben was attending their daughter's celebration from heaven. Then, she left the room, locking the door of her apartment behind her.

#

Four years after the wedding, Aurica and Aurel managed to save enough money to build a new house in Bucharest. The house was located on Georghe Manea Street. Aurica's brother, Adrian, helped them build the house after he graduated from law school. He took the left wing of the house, while Rosa moved into the right wing with the Rosenthals. They all lived together and raised Yossi.

When Adrian graduated, he was hired at the Danico, Mania and Partners law firm on Bulevardul Corneliu. He enjoyed working on special cases and became close friends with his coworkers. He ate breakfast every morning with his young nephew, Yossi, reading him the newspaper before going to work.

One wintry evening in 1941, just as Adrian was packing up to leave the office, the senior partner in the law firm stepped into his room. He locked the door behind him, his face pale. Adrian stiffened.

"Never mention this conversation to anyone," the lawyer said, his voice hushed.

Adrian nodded.

"And do not ask me any questions."

Adrian nodded again.

"I ask that you stay in my house tonight. If you do, your life will be saved."

"I'm sorry," Adrian replied, "I cannot. I must protect my mother and sister, my nephew, my neighbors, the community I grew up with. Though I do not know what will happen, I cannot abandon them."

"I see." The partner lowered his gaze. "If you will not take shelter in my house, take some advice. Do not leave your home, from the moment you return there tonight for the next forty-eight hours. Under any circumstances. You must barricade all the doors and windows. If possible, find a hiding place. Do not mention that you work here, not even under torture."

No further explanation was needed. The senior partner accompanied Adrian to the front door. His gaze was cold and stiff. Adrian refrained from thanking him, afraid someone would hear. Instead, he nodded sternly.

The next morning, on January 21, 1941, riots broke out across Bucharest. More than a hundred Jews were murdered and thousands of Jewish businesses, including synagogues, were looted and set on fire. The Rosenthals managed to wait out the storm, hidden in their storage area, with mattresses and cabinets pressed against the doors. Yossi slept the whole time, to the relief and prayers of his family.

#

Although his early childhood years were under the shadow of World War II and heavy discrimination, Yossi remembered a happy childhood. The rabbit doll that Grandma Rosa knitted for him was by his side, day and night. He loved listening to the bell of the horse-drawn carriages and talking to the gypsies, who would sell cream cheese and milk in brown pottery jugs. His mouth salivating, he would ask them for more, and they would always comply, rubbing his hair and teasing him for being so small.

His grandmother would let him sit on the counter when she baked, making his favorite apple pie cake, with apples on top and a layer of sweet cream on the bottom. He would climb the cherry tree that grew in their backyard and play with the puppy he received from his uncle, as a gift for his fifth birthday. He would walk down the streets of Bucharest, holding his mother's hand as she proudly waved to her friends and pointed to her smiling son, walking beside her. He enjoyed watching his mom standing on the porch in front of a canvas, her hair tied up high on her head, while she was immersed in the painting in front of her. Her smiling eyes illuminated his world.

Some bad memories were also engraved in his mind, but he could never tell if they were real or just nightmares. He remembered a huge closet in which he hid whenever heavy footsteps were heard ascending the stairs, followed by thunderous knocks on the door, accompanied by screams in German. He remembered his mother shaking and crying, his father holding her, while begging her to be quiet. He would sometimes wake up to the sounds of explosions, planes cutting the sky above, alarms ringing in his ears. Crying, Dad's soothing arms, a dark cave dug in the ground, people pushed over him into a pit. Uncle's voice whispering softly, and then he was back in his bed. Was it all nothing but a dream?

Yossi had a unique connection with his grandmother Rosa. The first thing that Yossi saw when he opened his eyes every morning was his grandma's smiling face. Her eyes were kind and her hands carried small surprises for him. He liked to cuddle up and listen to her stories. Grandma Rosa told stories of other places, of a distant town with a blue river flowing beside it. She loved to tell funny stories about herself from her childhood, about her parents, her four sisters, and her brother David. She told him of her mother, who was very talented, and of her father, whose heart was wide, brain was wise, and whose love for her Mama was eternal.

One day, about a month after Yossi turned two years old, he returned from pre-school and rushed to show his grandma the drawing he had made for her, but stopped when he saw tears streaming down her cheeks. Yossi was confused.

"Why are you crying, Grandma? Did you fall?"

She shook her head and pulled him into her lap. In her hands, she was gripping a letter so tightly, it was practically torn. He let her hug him until she was calm, and then he slipped away to play outside. A second before he left the room, he sent another glance at as to what the letter said, but was quickly distracted by the shouts of other children next door.

Aurica and Aurel's wedding, Bucharest 1930

Yossi and Grandmother Rosa, Vatra Dornei, 1946

CHAPTER SEVEN

Rosa,
1912, Piatra Neamț

At one point in the history of our town, the leaders decided, for administrative reasons, to divide the town into squares and call each street by a different name. Our house was called Domnitor Coza house No. 1.

About a month before I turned eighteen, the town's Jewish matchmaker, Mr. Fainaru, arrived at Domnitor Coza house No. 1, our home. Now that I was of age, I was expected to get married. As a young lady, it was up to my father to choose the right spouse for me. Marriages were often unsuccessful. My sisters and I pitied women who were forced to marry a horrible man, a drunken man, or a man they despised. Yet, the status of a woman being 'unmarried' was considered even worse.

Unmatched girls were considered "damaged" or "second-best." They ended up marrying widowers or lower-class men. Divorce or separation was unacceptable, as were second marriages. A woman whose husband died and left her a widow had to go back under the care of her parents until another widower agreed to marry her, if he needed her services.

Although I was nervous, thinking about giving up everything that was familiar to me and moving in with a man I knew nothing about, I wanted to make the process as easy for my family as possible. I did what was expected of me and trusted Tata to find the best match.

At the end of the marriage ceremony, the woman was expected to live in her husband's house, often in another town. Rarely did she reunite with her original family. I dreaded this, but knew I had to oblige.

Mr. Fainaru was a squat man. His eyes were adorned with thick glasses. Some days, the few hairs on his head were combed to the right. Other days, he combed them to the left. He always wore a brown suit that had seen better days. It was also several sizes too large for him; his hands barely protruded from his sleeves. He was known for his passion for homemade *Țuică*, a traditional drink made from plums and a lot of alcohol. Consequently, his body odor often smelled as if he had taken a bath in either plums or just straight alcohol. His house was modest and located up a stone path on the outskirts of town. Few people bothered to visit him.

No one knew how Mr. Fainaru started his matchmaking business in the Jewish community in our little town, nor his first name. Though he had never found himself a wife, he believed that "No one should be alone." Yet, he had no children to continue his tradition.

Fathers of prospective daughters were mostly concerned with finding suitable matches, preferably a spouse from a similar class who was deemed reliable. Tata was open to hearing our thoughts and promised not to give his consent without our approval.

When Mr. Fainaru came to our home that night, I touched Mama's ring in my pocket and prayed for someone to live a long life with.

Tata's meeting with the town matchmaker lasted about an hour. At the end of the meeting, and after I gave my approval with a nod, Tata gave his consent with a handshake and a glass of *Țuică.*

All I knew about my future husband was that his name was Reuben. He was a decent man who traded metal, which he loaded on a hay cart and wandered from town to town, trying to persuade people to buy from his goods. I found out that Reuben had no relatives and no house to return to. He agreed to stay for now at my family's house in Piatra Neamț. I was surprised, but happy. I was grateful to this stranger to whom I could be married and stay with my family.

The wedding took place in the small synagogue in town. At dusk, we gathered under a temporary canopy. The rabbi roared verses from the Torah, trying to overcome the noise of the stonecutter next door. I fingered the embroideries on the edges of my wedding dress, watching my feet. My sisters and I had worked for weeks before the wedding to create a simple cream-colored and modest wedding dress that could serve all five of us on our wedding days. We embroidered red flowers and geometric traditional designs to inspire a little joy in the stuffy room.

I looked nervously from under my veil and met David's kind eyes. He gave me a curt nod and I finally smiled. I glanced up at Reuben's face, who looked as nervous as me.

After the ceremony, we went back home. In the corner sat a long table, on which my sisters had laid down a handwoven cotton tablecloth, embroidered with floral patterns. We placed Challah bread, *Lekach*[15], and sweet pastries on the table. A small corner hosted a jug of wine for Kiddush. The few guests we had, left after an hour, satiated and joyful.

15 A sponge cake with honey.

David had vacated his room in the attic for the newlyweds. He found a corner in the basement of the house and turned it into his living space.

"I'm comfortable here," he lied.

I kissed his cheek and squeezed his hand. Following my new husband, we retreated to the attic.

#

In 1906, about two years after our wedding, I gave birth to my daughter. We named her Aurica. Two years later, we welcomed our son, Adrian, into the world. Jewish marriages were not recognized by the town government, and so no one recorded our union in any official document. My children were registered under my name, as if I were a single mother. But we were married in God's eyes and, for that, I was grateful.

#

A year after my wedding, Mr. Fainaru returned to our home. Feiga would soon turn 18. She was calm. Her only request was to find a decent groom, who would appreciate reading and writing. Moshe Wolf, a local farmer, who also served as the *Gabbai*[16] at the synagogue, was chosen as her match. Moshe was about ten years older than Feiga, an orphan with no relatives. He lived in a small wooden hut near the town of Botoșani, northeast of Piatra Neamț, to which Feiga returned with her husband, once the ceremony was over. In the pocket of her coat, which she wore over our family's wedding dress, she hid a booklet of "The Song of Songs." As the rabbi said his blessings, her fingers rubbed against the pages, reciting poetry in her mind.

16 A Gabbai is a person who is in charge of running the administrative operations of the synagogue.

When they returned to Moshe's home, Feiga opened her small suitcase, in which were some personal belongings and a couple of books.

"What are those?" Moshe asked, gesturing to the books.

"Poetry," Feiga whispered and looked down.

"Bialik's poems?" He picked up a book to examine it.

Feiga looked up, wide-eyed.

They spent the next several days reading poems about Zion, talking into the late hours of the night about their shared dreams.

"One day," Moshe promised, "we too will be pioneers, working the land, giving life, planting trees in the Promised Land." She looked at him with sparkling eyes, heart full.

Feiga and Moshe brought four children into the world. Isaac was the eldest son, then Shoshana. Abraham was born a year later, and the youngest son was named Hayim.

One cold morning, in early March, when the snow had already thawed but the spring had yet to come, Moshe went out as usual to work in the field. As soon as he loaded the sack of tools onto his shoulder, his heart stopped beating. He collapsed onto the ground. Isaac found his father's body lying close to the house under the apple tree. Feiga ran out to him and held her husband's body in her arms, screaming her sorrow to the sky.

Soon after, David escorted Feiga and her children back home to Piatra Neamț. Feiga refused to even consider re-marrying, shutting herself in her room and reading the poems her dear husband had once read to her as she went to sleep. "May you dream of our Zionist future, my love," Moshe would say, brushing dark curls out of her face.

David comforted Feiga through her mourning as she once did for him. During David's long recovery after his assault in the summer of 1901, Feiga sat by his bed and spent hours reading her favorite poems to him, even as he was unresponsive. Slowly, David woke to her voice, quietly repeating the words back.

Though his physical condition required rest, David refused to give up on his mental abilities. At first, he whispered syllables. Then he put them together and pronounced short words. Even when he finally got his speaking skills back, he had difficulty saying long words and had to divide each word into a few short syllables. Yet, he could recite poems easily.

While his physical condition improved and David was finally able to get out of bed, walking and standing were still difficult for him. He had to use a cane throughout his life. Despite his injuries, he hurried to the printing plant and asked for a job that would suit his skills. Tata joined him, and they both found jobs that supported the family.

Though David would have dinner with us every day after work, he would soon sneak back to his room. There, by the light of the oil lantern, he would dip a pen in ink and write his poems and thoughts onto white paper.

When David turned twenty-two, a coworker told him about a government stipend offered to students at Iași University, a university named after Domnitor Alexandru Ioan Cuza. "Only a few students manage to pass the entrance exams," the coworker warned, "and only one of those students wins this stipend." To apply to the Faculty of Literature, the candidate must send a collection from his own poetry writing.

The dim candlelight made it difficult for David to write, but he was tenacious. He dreamed of becoming a schoolteacher, and he was determined to make this dream come true, one way or the other.

A few months later, in late September 1911, David took the entrance exams.

He failed.

Around the same time, the matchmaker returned for Zilli. Her health had worried us since childhood, especially during the cold winter months. Her lungs were weak, and she had a troublesome cough that started with the first snowfall. Sometimes, she would faint and only wake up with the help of smelling salts. Other days her skin would suddenly be covered in red spots. These effects would improve and even disappear when the weather warmed up.

Thus, the matchmaking of Zilli was conditioned on one thing. The intended groom must take his bride to a warmer place of residence, preferably in a southern city, located by the sea.

Alexander, a dentist, with a short body and a large red face, was chosen to marry Zilli. He was from the town of Constanța on the shores of the Black Sea, where he owned a house on the southern shore, near Lake Techirghiol. This area was known for its concentrated minerals, salt water, and healing mud to strengthen the body and soul. Zilli left us, but we knew that she would be taken care of.

Not only did Zilli and Alexander's marriage go well, but his reputation as a leading dentist, with a central clinic on Ovidiu Square in the city center, benefited the newlyweds. They were included in high society and received invitations to attend the famous city's events. It was not long before the couple embraced an eldest son, named Pinku, followed by a beautiful daughter, named Yuly.

Reuben, my husband, worked hard. On the days he would leave on his trips, he would get up before sunrise and make himself a light breakfast. Then he would load the hay cart and go back on the road to sell his metal. A few weeks later, he would return exhausted, remove his straw hat and boots and leave the few coins he had managed to get in the metal jug in the kitchen. He then would shave his beard, kiss the children goodnight, and go to bed.

There were only short conversations between us. I never knew him well. He spoke softly, sitting by the fire and telling the children stories about people he met on his travels.

The money he brought back was used by the family to buy groceries and prepare food for the household. Tata and David also put the Lei they earned from their work in the printing plant in the same metal jug. We lived modestly, but lacked nothing.

#

One rainy afternoon in October 1913, a telegram arrived from a hospital a few towns away. It said, "Mr. Reuben Sofer-Isopovichi[17] has been in a terrible accident. He was kicked in the head by the horse carrying his cart. He has been taken to Timofei Moșneaga Hospital." I was in shock and quickly got my stuff ready to leave. David read the telegram as well, concerned that the telegram did not inform the family about Reuben's present condition.

David volunteered to take me to the hospital in the horse-drawn carriage. The trip took three days, due to heavy rainstorms. We curled up in our coats, stopping frequently so that the horses could rest too.

We finally reached our destination. The hospital was a large, red brick building with elongated windows. The entrance was made of a heavy wooden door with iron locks, reminiscent of an ancient monastery. It seemed as if it used to be an ancient church but now held a different set of prayers.

David leaned on his cane and pushed the door hard, until it opened with a terrible groan. I tightened my headscarf and looked down, afraid of what was about to come. A chill greeted us as we entered the large, gloomy room. Nurses in white gowns and hats hurried about. Hospital beds were placed one after the other in the room, separated by green faded curtains. Some big, gray curtains covered the windows and prevented the few rays of sun from entering the room.

17 Also spelled in Romanian as Iosubovici.

"Forgive me, Doamnă[18]," David politely addressed one of the nurses who passed by. "We are looking for Mr. Reuben Sofer-Isopovichi." The nurse measured David with her gaze and then pointed at a tall wooden desk that stood in the corner of the room.

"Ask there," she replied.

"Thank you." David raised his hat.

We approached the heavy wooden table at the other end of the room. A young nurse in a faded green apron and white nurse's hat sat behind the table. She did not look up, as she was writing furiously on a piece of paper. I watched her lips smack; the bright red lipstick smudged a bit around the edges. I rubbed my hands together to keep them warm.

"Excuse me, please," David asked politely.

The young nurse looked up grimly and stopped writing.

"I apologize for disturbing you, Doamnă," David said. "Maybe you could help us. We are looking for my brother-in-law, Mr. Reuben Sofer-Isopovichi. We learned he was injured, and we hoped we could see him today. We've come from far away," he added.

"Yes, sir," she said, her lips still pursed. "Wait here, please."

We watched as she walked down the dark hallway, clicking her heels.

"It's so cold here," I whispered and tightened the coat around my body.

David put his arm around my shoulder and sent me an encouraging look. "We'll be out of here soon," he whispered. "Let's see first what his condition is."

A few minutes later, the nurse came back and gestured for us to follow her.

We walked in silence through the dark corridor. The yellowish hue of the lamps emanating from the ceiling made us all look pale,

18 In Romanian meaning madam.

unhealthy. A few minutes later, we entered a smaller, quiet room. A strong smell greeted us. Ammonia mixed with salts, poppy, and other medicinal odors in the air.

The room contained about twelve beds, and on every bed, there was a patient. Not a sound left a single body. I shivered, terrified by how still and lifeless the bodies were.

"There," the nurse said, pointing to one of the beds near the window.

My body trembled. I was scared to get closer, of what I would find. David grabbed my elbow gently. "I'm here," he whispered.

As we approached, I could see Reuben's black hair sticking out from the pale sheets. His face was flushed, and his lips were gray. Tears filled my eyes. David hugged me and whispered, "You can cry. It's okay."

I never visited the hospital again. An acquaintance of David's from the printing factory happened to be in the area a few months later and inquired about Reuben's condition. The answer was, "Mr. Isopovichi is no longer with us."

I wrote to the hospital several times to try to find out where his body was resting, so we could say Kaddish on his grave, but my letters were never answered. For the rest of my life, I never knew if Reuben survived or died, or where his body might be. All I knew was that I had lost the man I was supposed to spend the rest of my life with.

#

When Elvira and Gisela turned eighteen, Mr. Fainaru visited the house once again.

Mr. Fainaru, as always, was equipped with a black notebook and a charcoal pencil where he kept his records. Rumor had it that before a baby turned a year old, Mr. Fainaru already knew who their match should be.

But this time, Mr. Fainaru was having trouble. Gisela and Elvira, who were only eight years old when our mother died, became so close to each other that they refused to separate, even now. Tata made the matchmaking contingent on finding two boys from the same town, so that even after their marriage, the sisters could live near each other.

The solution was finally found in the form of two young men from Bucharest, the bustling capital. One man, Isaac Stoleru, was a humble tailor, who came from a low-income family and made a living sewing suits and clothing for men. Victor Graur, the other match, was highly educated and came from a wealthier family. He worked as an accountant in the city. The two men met while playing soccer in the streets of Bucharest, and although their families were from different classes and never met, the two friends became inseparable.

Tata gave his blessing, and the matchmaking took place.

The two brides stood side by side and swore devotion to their husbands. At the end of the ceremony, they returned home and said goodbye in tears as they loaded their belongings. Soon, they were on their way to their new home in the big city.

I remained in Piatra Neamţ, raising my children and mourning my husband.

CHAPTER EIGHT

Friddie, 1940, Bucharest

After three days, Friddie returned home from the hospital. Her mind was in agony, hands clasped over the deflated skin on her stomach. Her child was gone, and she had not heard a word from Freddy.

Her parents brought her back to the empty apartment. Her mother went into the kitchen to get her a drink, as her father guided Friddie to her red armchair, his hands keeping her from collapsing. She sank into the armchair and hugged her knees in her hands. There was no need to speak, to say empty words. Her mother placed a strong alcoholic drink in her hands and covered her with a soft blanket. They sat across from her on the couch, holding each other's hands, but unable to hide the pain in their eyes.

After a while, her mother stood up, asking to open a window. Friddie whispered, "Don't." She curled up more. Her mother sat back down, looking concernedly at her husband. He nodded and squeezed his wife's hand. Finally, her parents left. They kissed her on the forehead, tucked the blanket in and closed the door quietly behind them.

A cat cried across the street. Her tears began to flow again. She didn't bother to wipe them away. She let them soak into the blanket, wet her clothes.

"Freddy, where are you?" she whispered into the still space. Darkness was kind to her. Silence was her friend.

When she opened her eyes, it was already morning. Through the closed shutter, she saw rays of sunlight. She shut her eyes, suppressing any attempt to let the light in. Finally, she surrendered. She opened her eyes. Her stomach ached and she remembered that she hadn't eaten for several days. Yet she wasn't hungry. She couldn't think about food. She glared angrily at the phone in the corner of the room, its stillness mocking her. Then she got up and walked to the bathroom. In the shower, she stared at her empty stomach. Her throat clenched and tears filled her eyes. She turned the water to cold and sobbed into the tiled sides.

She didn't know what to do now. The morning paper waited patiently at the front door, near to the lion statues. She picked it up from the floor and poured herself a cup of bitter coffee. She didn't bother to add sugar.

The morning headlines cried out, "There's no end to the war," "The king is gone," and, "The biggest economic crisis Romania has ever known. Who will save us?"

Where are you, Freddy? she pondered. She hadn't heard a word from him for almost four weeks. She didn't understand. In his previous travels, he always sent her a postcard, a telegram. Sometimes even a phone call. Phone calls were so terribly expensive and complex, especially in wartime, he explained before he left. Phone lines were not always in use and getting a call center to transfer private calls was harder now than ever. She understood that. She was satisfied with his letters, the kisses he showered when he returned. But where was he now? How would she tell him she'd lost their baby?

"Freddy, come home, please," she whispered to the empty living room. "I need you more than ever."

A few days passed, and she heard a knock on the door. Friddie hurried to answer it. "Freddy?" Her heart pounded loudly. "Is that you?" She was afraid to open the door, in case it wasn't him. What if it was a stranger? What if they brought bad news?

From the other side of the door, she heard a whisper. "Doamnă Karl?"

It was a deep masculine voice, but it was not Freddy's.

"Yes. Who are you?" Friddie asked

"*Domnul*[19] Karl told me to deliver something to you," he whispered. "I'm a friend of his. Please open the door."

With a trembling hand, she unlocked the door. She opened it just to a small slit and peered out. On the other side, she saw a young man, around 30, wearing a gray suit and black hat. She opened the door and let him in.

The man entered in silence and surveyed the house. "Is there anyone here, besides you?" he asked.

Friddie noticed that his voice was cold and his gaze sharp.

"No. There is no one else in the house," she whispered.

The man took off his hat. "Excuse me, madam, I cannot stay. I was asked to give you this." He took a brown envelope out of his coat.

"Thank you," she whispered. Her hands trembled as she held the envelope. The man hurried to put his hat back on.

"Wait... excuse me... I... I mean, maybe you know where Freddy is? I need to tell him something... I mean, when is he coming back home?"

"I'm sorry," said the stranger. "I have no information to give you. I was asked to give you this envelope and that's all. Maybe there's a letter inside? I'm sorry, I really don't know."

---

19 *Domnul* means sir or Mr. in Romanian.

The man opened the door and raised his hat again.

"Thank you," said Friddie, but he had already hurried away.

Friddie held the envelope. She sat down at the dining table and placed it on the table gently. She moved it around the table, spinning it in circles. Placing her hand on the top of it, her fingers spread across the surface, she pressed down. It felt soft and compressed easily underneath her hands. She slowly removed her fingers and bit her nails, continuing to stare at the envelope.

She turned the envelope over, but there was no address, no name, nor a postage stamp. The envelope had apparently changed hands until it reached its destination. Perhaps Freddy had written her some letters and stuffed them all in this envelope. Then he must have found a way to get them to her, through some network of strange men. Had Freddy's fingers touched the envelope? Did his fingers tremble when he sealed it? Maybe there was a letter from her lost husband, explaining his delay. Maybe there was no secret at all.

She grabbed a kitchen knife and sliced open the envelope very gently, as if a treasure were hidden inside. Her fingers reached inside and began to pull out sheets of paper.

Money. There were different types of bills: Lei, American dollars, and British pounds. More cash, more bills. A lot of them. Friddie placed them on the table, one by one, looking for a letter inside. But none was there.

Friddie didn't know what to do. She called her parents and asked them to come over. She showed them the brown envelope and pile of cash. Then her Tanti Gisela and her husband Victor were called. They had a well-known social status in the city, maybe they would be able to help. But now, during the war, even Victor had lost many of his social and business connections. None of his acquaintances who were still willing to help knew anything about a perfume factory located in Bucharest that would send scientists to do research about fragrances. Especially during wartime. They would raise their eyebrows and ask about the missing man, but beyond that, they could do nothing.

Friddie also sought the advice of her beloved Tanti Rosa. She and her family came over once to help. Her cousin Aurica and husband Aurel brought their toddler, Yossi, with them. They hugged her, cried with her, but were helpless, just the same. Aurel advised her to keep the cash under her bed, not to deposit it in the bank, because banks may go bankrupt during wars. He told her that if she ever needed to bribe someone to save herself, only cash and diamonds would work.

Friddie hugged baby Yossi and wiped away a tear. The joy of life that was in this child and the curiosity with which he explored every corner of Friddie's apartment made her happy. "May you always be the smartest and most curious you can be," she whispered in his ears. It is doubtful that Yossi understood at such a young age what his mother's cousin was saying. He hurried to jump from her knees and chase a howling cat that suddenly entered the yard.

A few weeks later, Friddie received another brown envelope. This time, the envelope was shoved under the apartment's door, while Friddie was out running errands. This envelope, just as the previous one, was filled with Lei, American dollars, and some British pounds. The envelope again didn't contain a letter, a stamp, or any handwriting. Friddie added those bills to the hiding place under her mattress. There was still no trace of Freddy.

The third envelope came about a month later, once again clear of handwriting. It was a brown envelope, no letters, no notes, just another pile of bills. This envelope was shoved under her door in the middle of the night, while Friddie was sleeping. She didn't hear any knocks on the door and only found the envelope early the next morning.

The fourth envelope shoved under Friddie's door, a month later, contained no bills. Friddie's heart was beating happily as she found a short note typed by a typewriter machine on a bright white paper.

Friddie hurried to open the folded letter. "Meet me tomorrow, 6:45 a.m., at the main post office on Calea Victoriei, next to mailbox #67. Come alone. Don't tell anyone. Waiting for you." A shiver of cold sweat went through her body. Freddy. She had no doubt he wrote the note. She could feel it in her guts. He's probably in danger and needs my help, she thought. Freddy was back, and she would see him tomorrow. He would explain everything. She would understand. She would bring him home. She would forgive him for being away for so long.

Friddie was overjoyed. No more money tucked in an envelope; her Freddy was finally home. Tears of joy filled her eyes. God, how much she missed him, cuddling in his arms, feeling safe again. She yearned for his loving gaze, his soft lips. Freddy. Her Freddy.

Friddie could barely sleep that night. Her heart was pounding. He wrote, "Come alone." He had used a typewriter to hide his identity. What had happened? Why wouldn't he just come back to their apartment, their home? He wrote, "Waiting for you." If only he knew how long she had been waiting for him. It had been almost six months since he left. "I'll wait for you forever," they had promised each other, more than once. What was six months, compared to eternity?

At 5:30 the next morning, she hurried to the shower. She put on light makeup and wrapped herself in the perfume that Freddy loved the most, the lilac perfume. The fragrance she had worn the night they met. She put on a white dress and high heels, like a bride waiting for her groom. She brushed her hair and remembered the night she was supposed to marry Nelu. She could still feel his disappointment, the heartbreak she had caused her family. The sense of relief she had gained. She met Nelu a year later, while he was embracing another young girl. She introduced him to Freddy and felt more honest, happy. She wished him all the best. She told him she hoped he would find happiness, as she had found hers.

She made herself a cup of coffee and drank it slowly, waiting for the time to pass. Thoughts were racing through her head, as if they were running a marathon. At 6:20 a.m., she couldn't wait any longer. She left the house, locked the door, and started walking towards the main post office in the city. The walk was short, less than fifteen minutes away. Friddie felt as if she was flying. Her feet were floating above the ground, swallowing the distance.

The post office building was a simple government building that had served its customers faithfully throughout the years. Tired official clerks, starting their workday not before 9:00 a.m., usually sat at heavy wooden tables, waiting for customers. Right now, it was too early, and the place was empty. Outside the building, on the north side of the lot, were lockers made out of metal, where heavy packages were placed, waiting for recipients to come and pick them up.

Friddie arrived at the post office building. Her heart pounded hard. She took a deep breath and her lips mouthed, "Freddy." Her face flushed with excitement. She could smell the trees after the rain. She could hear birds singing for their reunion. Suddenly, an iron gate squeaked open. The birds erupted into the sky in a mad dash. Friddie decided not to let the noise ruin her moment. She kept walking, looking around, searching for his familiar face. She saw locker #121. She needs to look for #67. Keep walking, her mind cried. Almost there, just a few more steps. Her eyes flickered everywhere, looking for the box, looking for a familiar face. Finally, she found #67, but no one was there. No living soul in the entire area. She felt disappointment seeping into her, pressing her forehead into the locker.

Out of nowhere, two men rushed towards her. One of them was holding a gun, aiming it at her. What was going on here? She stepped backward, mouth agape. Someone grabbed her arm tightly. "Mrs. Karl?" he asked.

"Yes?" she whispered.

"Come with us. You're under arrest."

"What? Why? What the hell is going on here?" she shouted. "I didn't do anything! Leave me alone. Let me go!" She screamed as she tried to free herself from his grip.

"You're under arrest!" one of them spat in her face. "You betrayed your homeland. Now shut up and come with us!"

"No! Wait a minute. That's a mistake," Friddie screamed. "Impossible. Wait. Leave me alone. Freddy!" Friddie screamed with all her might. "Freddy! Help me!"

The darkness enveloped around her as she collapsed onto the ground, feeling her head smashing against the hard concrete floor.

#

Friddie opened her eyes to darkness. She was confused. Where was she? Was it a dream? Her head was resting on a stiff surface and her body was in a chair. She felt pressure on her eyes. Instantly, she tried to touch her face, but her hands were tied with a rope behind her back.

"What's going on? Where am I?"

"Good morning, Mrs. Karl." She heard a cold, metallic sound behind her. "I'm glad you woke up. We've been waiting for you," said a voice.

Friddie lifted her head off the table and tried to straighten up in the chair. "What's going on?" she asked again. Her eyes were covered.

She heard footsteps approaching and suddenly the cloth was torn off her face.

She groaned and tried to rub her eyes. The rope wore at her wrists.

Slowly, Friddie opened her eyes and looked around. She was in some kind of a shelter, made of cold concrete with exposed walls.

Close to her was a desk made of dark brown wood, on which stood a table lamp. The light in the room was dim. A man approached her.

"Do you remember me, Mrs. Karl?" he said and stood in front of her.

"Yes..." Friddie tried to remember. The face was familiar and so was his voice. How the hell do I know him? she wondered. She looked around. On the hanger rack in the room hung a long black coat and, next to it, a man's high black hat. And then, suddenly, she remembered. "Yes. You're the man who brought me the envelope from Freddy. You were at my house a few months ago… You said you're a friend."

"That's right, Mrs. Karl. I see you remember very well. It will only help the investigation."

"Investigation? What investigation?" Friddie asked. "Where am I?"

"Mrs. Fridda Karl, patience. We'll get to that. But first, some rules. I'm asking the questions here. Do you understand? If you cooperate, you can go home soon. Otherwise, you stay here. Is that clear to you?"

Friddie was too scared to respond. She looked around. The man, this stranger who came to her house only a few months ago, was relatively short. He had a narrow physique but with broad shoulders. His hair was pitch-black and his eyes were dark. She also noticed a gun tucked into his belt. He wore plain gray pants and a black button-down shirt.

"Where is Freddy, maybe you can tell me that?" she begged.

The man's mouth twisted and he slapped her, hard. She cried out in pain, trying to hide her face in her hands. But the rope around her wrists caught them again.

"Do not play games with me. Do you understand? I ask the questions. You answer. Do you understand the rules, or do I have to explain myself again?" He raised his hand as if about to slap her again.

Friddie quickly turned her head away. "No. Please," she said.

"Good. I see we have reached an agreement." He went to the chair by the desk and sat down. Friddie noticed that there were blank papers and some pens scattered on the table. The man sat down and picked up a pen in his hand.

"Let's start again. Begin with some simple details. What's your name?"

"Fridda Karl," she replied through her tears.

The man wrote her name at the top of the page. "And before you became Mrs. Karl, what was your maiden name?"

"Stoleru, Fridda Stoleru."

His pen scribbled across the page.

"And what's your residential address?"

Friddie gave him her address, even though it was clear he knew where her apartment was located, since he had visited her recently.

Just then, the door opened. Heavy footsteps entered.

The stranger raised his head to the door. "Detective Chernovik. Just in time! Come join us. Please meet Mrs. Fridda Karl," the man said. "This is Detective Chernovik, and I am Detective Stalie."

Detectives? Friddie wondered. Did that mean she was at a police station? She was afraid to ask and be slapped again.

Friddie studied the second detective, hoping to find some mercy in his face. Detective Chernovik was a broad man with brown hair, brown eyes. A gray mustache covered the bottom half of his face. The two men were not wearing police uniforms. Suddenly, a new fear began to creep into her head. Friddie had heard of people going missing into black cars. Witnesses said the kidnappers acted like the police. Have I been grabbed by the secret police? she wondered, chewing her lip while staring at the two men. The broader man was hitting his hip with a leather whip. What did they want to do with her?

The men turned to her, the smiles on their faces twisting into something terrifying. Detective Stalie held her shoulders and rained questions down on her. When she didn't know the answer, or the answer did not satisfy them, she received a variety of blows, kicks, and whips from the other policeman.

"Who is this man?" they screamed and slapped Freddy's picture on the table. She gaped at her husband, shaking her head.

"That is my husband! He's a perfumer, traveling the world in search of a new scent. That's all I know! All he's told me!"

"No! He's a traitor! A spy! He sells our secrets to our enemies!"

"No, you're wrong!" she pleaded. "He is my husband. He is a good man. He works hard for a living. I'm his only family here. That's all I know." Her chest ached with sobs.

"Traitor!" they screamed at her and beat her with the whip. "You're a spy, just like him! Disgusting creature!"

Friddie found herself lying on the floor, blood seeping from cuts all over her body. She had lost consciousness several times and this was her latest awakening. She dreaded waking up, and what would come next. The powerful kicks had already broken her ribs. Her mouth tasted bitter.

She had stopped trying to answer their questions hours earlier. Her whole body was on fire. Friddie lay on the floor and let them do as they pleased. They could break her body, but not her mind, she thought. She lost any attempt to find order and logic in her current situation. There was no point in trying to understand. Whenever she tried, she was beaten.

Night must have come, for they brought her to a cell, towards the back of whatever building they were in. Detective Stalie threw her on the cold concrete floor. The other detective threw a metal bucket in the corner of the cell. "So you can clean yourself up," he growled.

The cell was cold, empty. An old mattress was tossed in a corner, smelling of other people's waste. Friddie stumbled onto it with the rest of her strength, curled against the prickly straw, and let the darkness surround her. "Freddy," her lips formed his name quietly as she fell asleep. "Save me, Freddy."

#

After some time, two guards came and dragged her to the interrogation room. Friddie had no idea what time it was, though she assumed morning had come. There was no light in the room, nor a clock. The white dress she had worn the day before to meet Freddy was taken from her. She had woken up to find a faded gray-striped gown in the entrance of her cell. With Detective Stalie screaming at her to get dressed, she quickly threw the gown over her head. It felt thick with dirt, uncleaned since its last wearer.

They seated her in the wooden chair, tied her hands behind her back with a thick rope and left the room. Why they took such precautions, she did not know. Her body ached all over and her legs were too weak to stand on their own.

"Eat it." She jerked and looked up. She saw Detective Stalie in front of her, a table between them. He threw a piece of dry bread in front of her. "Eat," he commanded. Friddie's hands were tied behind her back. She brought her face closer to the slice of bread on the table and chewed, her jaw working the stale bread like a cow chewing grass. She licked the breadcrumbs from the table with her tongue. Detective Stalie looked away, grimacing with disgust.

"Mrs. Karl," he said, "I want to try to ask you some questions again. I will try to be nice, but please remember that my patience is short."

Friddie's body began shaking. She nodded, licking the crumbs off her lips.

"Where is Mr. Karl now?"

"Please," Friddie begged as tears flooded her eyes. "I don't know. I haven't seen him in over six months. I really don't know. That's the truth. I promise."

"Liar." He whipped her face with a ruler from behind his back. "I don't believe you. Try again."

Friddie felt blood burst from her lips.

"Please," she begged again, tears and blood dripping off her chin. God help me, she thought desperately.

Detective Stalie placed a picture on the table in front of her. "Let's see if this will refresh your memory." He grabbed the back of her neck and brought her face closer to the picture. "What do you see here?" he barked.

Friddie looked at the picture through her tears. It was a black-and-white picture, showing Freddy, smiling at someone behind the camera. "Is that your husband?"

Friddie saw his face, his thin lips, his dimples, his enchanting brown eyes. "Yes," she nodded.

"Now, look at this." The detective threw another picture on the table. His hand still held the back of her neck, fingers squeezing around her flesh. "Who do you see in this picture?"

This picture was also in black and white. It looked like a normal picture that was taken at some social event. Freddy was surrounded by a group of men, grinning and holding a glass of wine. All of the men were wearing fancy suits, like those the men would wear to the dance club. She remembered the club, hanging in Freddy's arms as he twirled her around to a slow song. She gulped.

"Do you know anyone here?" asked the inspector.

"No. Just my husband."

"Yes, your husband and… Anyone else?"

Friddie hesitated for a moment. She surveyed the faces again. She could not identify anyone else, and she knew the detectives would not be happy.

"I'm sorry," she said apprehensively.

The detective hit her with the ruler again. "Liar!" he screamed. "They are all your friends, aren't they? They all cooperate with you and your husband. They are agents, traitors, spies, and filthy animals. Just like you!"

Lines of pain stung across her face. They would never be happy with her, no matter what she said. They would never let her go. They were convinced she was a spy. They wanted answers, but she had no answers to give them, because she was not who they thought she was. She could not convince them otherwise, and the more she resisted, the more they believed she was just being dishonest.

The detective kicked the chair legs out from under her. Her head hit the table and she fell to the floor. "Let's see if we can jog your memory," Detective Stalie snarled in her ear. He hit her, kicked her in the stomach, and whipped her back. Her sobs echoed around the interrogation room. She spat blood onto the floor, begging God to let her lose consciousness. Friddie wanted darkness to be her friend again.

Detective Chernovik reappeared. He kneeled down beside her and said, "Well, shall we keep going, darling?" He grabbed her armpits and threw her into the chair. The detective's face was red from the effort, and he gasped slightly.

"Let's see another picture, shall we?" Detective Stalie threw another picture on the table, again grabbing the back of her neck. He shoved her closer to the image. "Tell us, Mrs. Karl, what's in this picture?"

Friddie was already staring at the picture, her mind racing. This photo showed a couple walking down the street, holding hands and smiling at each other. The man was undoubtedly Freddy. She would recognize him from miles away. But beside him was a blonde woman, looking at Freddy with wide and lovestruck eyes. On Freddy's shoulders sat a brunette boy, perhaps about three or four years old, with his hands in the air. The woman was holding the hand of a young girl with long, blonde hair. Friddie's heart shuddered violently. The children looked awfully like Freddy.

"What do you have to say about this picture, Mrs. Karl?" The detective lit a cigarette and blew the smoke into Friddie's face. "Who do we have in this picture now?"

"I don't know," she said, her voice barely above a whisper. "Maybe his sister, maybe other relatives?" Friddie didn't understand. After all, Freddy told her that he had no family other than his mother, who returned to Germany when he was in a boarding school, after his father had died. He never mentioned siblings. Was this his sister? Perhaps a distant cousin?

"So, let me tell you." Detective Stalie brought his mouth to her ear and whispered, "This is the real Mrs. Karl. Yes, this is our Mr. Karl's real wife. And there, you see? On his shoulders? This is Mr. Karl's real son. He's a nice boy. And the little girl is their daughter. Nice family, right? Do you see how similar they all look? Well..." He continued, "That picture was taken about a year ago. We need to know where he is. We need to find him now."

Friddie's heart pounded. This was impossible. Friddie was Freddy's wife. He had married her. He swore to be faithful to her until death. She promised to wait for him for eternity. It was a lie. It was not real. They were playing with her, with her heart, with her mind. They abused her and lied to her for no reason. She refused to believe them.

"You see, Mrs. Karl," the detective whispered into her ear, his lips pressed against the side of her head. "If this is the real Mrs. Karl, in this picture, then what does it make you?"

"It can't be Freddy," she said finally, looking at the detective with her brows furrowed. "It's not real. It can't be. Freddy will explain it to you when he comes home."

"Oh, and by the way," Detective Stalie added after a minute, with sarcasm in his voice, "since your dear husband was already married to another lady, at the same time he married you, I took the liberty to annul your marriage. Here is your certificate of annulment." He slammed a piece of paper in her face.

She no longer felt the lashes, kicks, and blows to her battered body. She lay on the cold concrete floor, letting the darkness back in.

#

Time lost all meaning to Friddie as she was interrogated and tortured. Her only relief came at night when she was thrown back into her cell. There, she would curl on top of the sagging mattress. In the dark corner, she tried to put the pieces together.

She refused to believe that Freddy was a traitor, a spy, or selling Romania's secrets to the enemy. But she didn't understand the pictures the detective had shown her, either. Freddy and this woman she did not know, with children that looked like him. Perhaps he had a family, and something terrible had happened to them, Friddie reasoned.

Yet, he never mentioned any family at all. Or his past, she realized. Whenever she had tried to be honest about her past wrongdoings, he would say, "Forget the past. Let us focus on our future," and kiss her deeply. But even if he had done something terrible, she would accept and forgive with love. "Please just come home, Freddy," she would whisper into the darkness. "Come save me."

#

She barely felt the physical abuse that came every day. They kicked her, beat her with a whip. Their questions repeated between hits. She no longer tried to answer, to beg to be released, to be trusted. There was no point in it, she knew. She gave up. She missed her family, her parents, her aunts, and her friends. Her poor parents; surely they worried so much now. If only they knew where she was, if only she could call them, let them know she was still alive.

Once every couple of days, she was allowed to shower in cold water. She received a portion of bread and a cup of water in her cell around the same time. She ate and drank like an animal. Her mind was quickly unraveling with pain and loneliness. She saw no one else but the two interrogators and dreaded every day. At night, she would talk to Freddy, telling him about an imaginary day when they walked on the beach in Eforie Nord for hours. As the detectives let loose their rage on her body, she would add aspects to her perfect day, excited to share it with Freddy as she drifted into sleep.

One day, a young nurse came to her cell, as if by mistake. She had a delicate face, clear skin, and light blue eyes. She was wearing a white robe and a nurse's hat. Friddie opened her eyes and saw her, as if an angel had appeared in front of her.

"Poor thing," whispered the nurse. "What have they done to you?"

"Did I die?" Friddie whispered back. She gaped at the figure in white.

"No, my darling." The nurse smiled, and helped Friddie get into a sitting position. The nurse's eyes were kind. With delicate fingers, she checked over Friddie's wounds. Friddie noticed there was a sheet of paper next to the nurse and, from time to time, the nurse wrote things down on it.

At the top of the page was written in bold letters: Fridda Karl, Prisoner 38579560.

"Who are you?" Friddie muttered to the angel, whose hands were gently touching a wound on her forehead that hadn't yet healed.

"My name is Christiana," whispered the nurse. "I'm here to help you."

The nurse cleaned Friddie's wounds with a cloth that she would periodically rinse in a bowl of cold water. She then applied an ointment to Friddie's wounds that made them burn and covered them with bandages. Occasionally, she murmured, "Poor thing, poor thing."

When she finished, she hurried to write something on the sheet in front of her.

"Thank you," Friddie mumbled.

"I'm so sorry." The nurse looked down. "If there was anything I could do..."

"I have a small favor to ask." Friddie sat up quickly and grabbed the woman's sleeves.

"I'm not sure I can help," the nurse whispered. "They don't tell us anything. Do you understand?" She turned to leave, but then stopped and looked at the crumbs on the floor, the only evidence that Friddie was being fed.

"No, no, please! I have to talk to someone, see a human face. This loneliness is unbearable! I'm going crazy," Friddie sobbed.

"I can't do anything," the nurse whispered and looked towards the door. She hugged the sheet of paper to her chest. "I wish I could. I'm so sorry." She rushed away. Friddie stared at the door for a while, and then curled up on the mattress once again.

When Friddie opened her eyes again, she smelled something peculiar. Delicious. Sitting up, she looked around for the source of the aroma. In the corner of the room, a hot bowl of soup sat next to some blank sheets of paper and a black ink pen. Attached to the sheets of paper was a note that read, "Write down your thoughts. Create a new world for yourself."

CHAPTER NINE

Rosa, 1914, Iași

Iași, the capital of the province of Moldova, was located in northeastern Romania. It was considered a liberal haven, the perfect place for artists and intellectuals to find their home. Including David.

The city was actually a port city, where goods would transfer from Poland to Bessarabia. Colorful and extravagant architecture decorated the streets. A rich cultural life, nurtured gardens, world-famous opera houses and theaters, entertainment centers, luxury restaurants, clubs, and a cosmopolitan atmosphere. All of this made Iași the city of David's dreams.

More than anything, Iași University became the focal point of his fantasies. The University of Iași was established in 1860 and was considered the center of modern Western liberal philosophical thinking. Lectures were open to the public, poetry readings filled the nights, and theater performances and concerts attracted many visitors to the university. Even on the coldest of nights, people swarmed the campus to see what it could offer.

At first, only three faculties were established at the university: philosophy, theology, and law. However, the faculties of literature, science, and medical studies were added to the list soon after.

David longed to study literature. Though he had failed the entrance exam, he knew that Iaşi was the city of his dreams. So, he tried his luck again. A year after failing the entrance exams, he took them again. He waited anxiously, barely able to concentrate at the printer's shop. The letter finally arrived at our house in Piatra Neamţ. He opened the letter, his fingers gripping the envelope tightly. His hands trembled and his pulse accelerated until he reached the words, "We are happy to inform you of your acceptance." Tears of joy flowed down his cheeks.

He hid the letter deep inside his jacket and hurried to the printing house.

We were all happy for David. I, still the optimist I have always been, believed that dreams were meant to come true. But David, who had always been more realistic, feared for the family's financial state. Even though he had received a government scholarship to attend the university, he knew the loss of income of an additional breadwinner would harm the family's financial situation, which was already unstable. Tata's sight was fading, which he kept hidden so he would not lose his job at the printing house. He could no longer read from the newspaper without help. "We'll get along," I promised David, urging him to leave. Gisela and Victor, who now lived in Bucharest and were financially stable, promised to support the family. Feiga, who repaired men's hats, also managed to put some coins in the metal jug in the kitchen.

With great hesitation, David packed his belongings. Tears swelled in his eyes as he said goodbye to us at the train station. Within a few hours, he arrived at the train station in Iaşi. Excitement enveloped him as he got off the train. He had never seen such long, almost never-ending streets, separated by rows of elongated buildings, dressed in white stones, prolonged windows, intricate rooftops and steeples that adorned the magnificent churches. David stood there for a while, observing this glorious new atmosphere.

"Watch out," someone shouted at him, and metal screamed behind his back.

David managed to jump to the side and saw the electric tram rushing away, not far from where he had stood, seconds ago.

He breathed a sigh of relief and straightened the jacket he was wearing. The streets were bustling with life; crowds of people passed by. Horse-drawn carriages hurried off, alongside people and merchants announcing their wares. Women in floral dresses and colorful hats and men in custom-made suits scurried past him. The sun warmed the streets.

As he walked towards the university, street traders approached him and asked if he was interested in buying something, or perhaps having his shoes polished. David politely declined, keeping the few coins in his pocket for dinner.

He crossed the long shopping streets and turned right. The university appeared in front of him, the buildings rising into the air like huge brick trees. At the entrance, there were several tall statues of great Romanian leaders. Above them all stood a statue made of heavy limestone, a depiction of the great Alexandru Ioan Cuza. David wandered through the intricate paths, nodding to fellow students, who meandered in and out of the seven main buildings. A spacious green lawn greeted him, which he crossed to reach the university plaza.

"Excuse me, sir." David turned to a young man, who hurried to cross the gate on a bicycle.

"Yes?"

David presented him with the letter of acceptance.

"You must be looking for the Literature building." The young man smiled and immediately pointed to a smaller building. "Look for Professor Piscu on the second floor." The young man hurried to get on his bike and sped away before David could even thank him.

David went to the heavy door and pushed it open. Loud noises from within poured out from the entrance, breaking the silence of the plaza. Students rushed between rooms. Cheerful bursts of laughter and shouts of joy filled the hallways, as doors opened and closed. Young people dashed up and down the stairs, wearing tailored jackets and ties, carrying loads of books in their arms. David noticed that some female students also occasionally ran by.

David, who had recently turned twenty-four, felt mature compared to the rest of the young and carefree students. He knew that, in order to maintain the government scholarship, he would have to devote his whole self to his studies; in addition, he promised to send money to his family, who remained in Piatra Neamț. He would have to get a job soon. No, he would not have time for recreational activities. He was not free, only somehow new. Taking a deep breath, he pictured our family back in our small house and the almost empty jug.

He hurried up the stairs to the registration office.

About an hour later, David left the building with a note and the residential address assigned to him.

#

Slowly, David adapted to the big city. His roommate was a young, liberal, fast-talking, red-haired man. He quickly stopped inviting David to spend time at the students' club. They spent most of their time outside the room, and hardly talked after the first week of classes.

David worked hard. He spent his free time hanging out at the university library. He found a job as a private tutor. He was happy teaching young people to read and write. He especially enjoyed sharing the mysteries of Latin, so similar to Romanian, yet so hard to grasp. As he promised, the money he earned, he put in an envelope and sent home to Piatra Neamţ.

One day, David visited the home of one of his favorite students, Clara. Clara had recently turned nine years old. She was born disabled, unable to move below her waist. She spent her days in a wheelchair and never attended school. Her father, who was a chemistry professor at the university, loved his only daughter with all his heart and made sure to give her a proper education. He hired private tutors (students from the university) and paid them generously to teach Clara what she would typically learn at school.

Clara liked David. They bonded over their physical limitations. David still dragged his right foot and used a cane. Clara hoped that one day she could get up from her wheelchair and walk. "Perhaps with a cane, like you, David!" she would giggle.

"How about you write your wishes on the page?" David suggested and laid a blank page in front of her. Clara accepted the challenge.

At the top of the page, she wrote the word, "Dreams".

"Excellent," David encouraged her.

"I had a dream to fly in the sky," she wrote.

"Beautiful," he said. "Like what?"

"...Like a butterfly!" she said. She erased the words "in the sky" and wrote, "like a butterfly."

"And what's the color of this butterfly?"

"Yellow and brown," she wrote. "He is a curious one, whose eyes can actually hear."

"What do they hear?" he asked.

"The music of the world," she replied, and wrote it down in big letters.

At the end of the lesson, David hurried down the stairs. "Bye, Clara!" he shouted. He was late to his next tutor obligation, having lost track of time with Clara. He was never late and hoped his next student would not be mad at his tardiness. As his hand touched the doorknob, the door swung open.

"Sophie!" Clara shouted happily.

A beautiful, tall woman ran straight into David. He stumbled and looked up at his assailant. She apologized profusely and then giggled at his awestruck face.

Sophie's long hair was gathered in a ponytail and her eyes watched David with interest. She wore a purple shirt and a light skirt that accentuated her gorgeous figure.

David could not take his eyes off her. "Ah... pleasure to meet you," he finally recovered and reached for words.

Sophie shook his hand. "Sophia Albescu," she laughed.

David later learned that Sophie, a second-year student studying music, was orphaned at a young age. She too was lonely here in the city of Iași, busy working to support herself. She relied on the university scholarship and private music lessons she gave to local children.

The weeks passed, and David could think of nothing but Sophie. Each time he finished his lessons with Clara, he slowed down, so he could meet Sophie again.

His joy knew no bounds when Sophie finally agreed to accompany him to the theater. He spent a little money on a used suit and picked her up twenty minutes early. She never stopped teasing him for this.

Soon, Sophie and David started spending all their free time together. Love blossomed and David asked her to marry him as soon as they graduated. David and Sophie continued to excel in their studies. David knew that his dream of becoming a schoolteacher was about to come true. Sophie hoped to become a music teacher for children. They had no idea the world was about to burst, disturbing all of their plans.

#

The assassination of the Austro-Hungarian Duke Franz Ferdinand in July 1914 marked the beginning of the First World War. For a long time, Romania tried to remain neutral. Finally, in 1916, after signing an agreement with the treaty countries, Romania joined the effort and declared war on the Central Powers (Austro-Hungary, Germany, Bulgaria, and the Ottoman Empire).

Over a million men between the ages of eighteen and forty-five enlisted in the military by government order. Under the leadership of Romanian King Ferdinand I, the Romanian army was divided into four sections. While three armies turned to northeastern Romania towards Transylvania, the Fourth Army headed south, to protect Romania's borders from the possibility of a Bulgarian attack. During the war, Bucharest was occupied, and Iași took its place as the temporary capital city. Government ministries were transferred to Iași.

Although Romanian Jews were never granted citizenship, 23,000 Jewish men joined the Romanian army and fought, side by side, with their Romanian brothers. The battles were fierce. Many soldiers were killed, and others were captured or went missing. Schools, churches, and synagogues were temporarily converted to hospitals. The shortage of weapons and food was felt at the front, as well as among the residents left behind.

David was drafted into the army, despite his physical limitations. The night before he left for the front, he met Sophie and took her into his arms. Sophie cried into his chest. "Promise me," she whispered, "promise me you will come back to me." David sealed his promise with a kiss.

David was seriously injured but survived. A bullet pierced his right knee, in the same leg that was injured before, and he was taken to a field hospital, just a few miles from Piatra Neamț. The doctor who operated on him on the battlefield under the blue sky was a third-year medical intern from the Faculty of Medicine at Iași. He recognized David from the library and they became close friends, playing cards across his bed.

The war ended in November 1918, and David returned to Sophie. His leg was amputated but he proudly wore the King's *bravery medal*[20]. They went back for their final school year.

Soon after his return, David turned twenty-nine. He kept his promise and married Sophie back at home in Piatra Neamț. She even wore our family's wedding dress. The rabbi said his blessings and they spent the night in our family home. We were finally able to be back together.

20 The medal is called Commemorative War Cross (1916 – 1918) and was instituted in 1918. It was awarded to military personnel for superior service during the Great War.

CHAPTER TEN

Friddie,
1943, Somewhere in Prison

My dearest mom and dad,

I hope this letter will miraculously find its way to you.

It has been two years since I was taken from you.

Please, do not worry about me. I was arrested by the police and charged with a crime I did not commit.

Please forgive me for all the grief I have caused. I'm trying to stay strong. I still believe in compassion, in justice, in the kindness of mankind, just like you taught me. I long for the day I'm free again, the moment when we can finally meet again. I believe in miracles.

Embracing you in my thoughts and sending you lots of love.

I miss you.

Friddie

Friddie finished the letter and kissed the page. She took a moment to cuddle up with her memories of the past. Her parents' house rose in her mind, the smell of freshly baked *albinita*[21] filling the house with sour honey. A younger Friddie ran down the stairs, her mother picking her up and shoving some cake into her mouth. That had happened years ago, when she believed evil only existed in stories.

"Stop that." She became angry with herself. She had to repress such thoughts from her mind, otherwise she would go crazy. No longer did she talk to Freddy in her mind. She had almost forgotten about him.

Friddie folded the letter and placed it under the mattress. Then she looked at the pile of blank papers left in her hands. She must do something, otherwise she would lose her sanity. She placed the pen on the paper and let the words flow.

BLUE-WING BIRD

By Fridda Karl (Somewhere in Prison, 1943)

A small little bird, a free sparrow
Spread your wings and fly away,
Wander to the distance, to the familiar places
Taste the water of the well-known river of happiness.

See how much beauty there is in the world.
The shingles of the red houses gleaming in the rays of the sun.
The scents of the flowers washed in the dew water.
The delicate hands scatter breadcrumbs.
The laughter of children who know no worries.

They will come for you, my dear little sparrow
Shatter your innocence and pull your heart out
They will crush your skull with stones
Shatter the wings of imagination you worked so hard to create.
Do not forgo, my blue-winged bird
Do not succumb to the forces of evil.
They, wishing for your downfall,
Will eternally grasp the pain of their mortal end.

CHAPTER ELEVEN

Rosa, 1918, Piatra Neamț

One morning the town awoke to rising cheers coming from the main street. World War I had finally ended, and the soldiers began to return home.

"Rosa, Feiga," Tata happily exclaimed. "Come on, look!"

I wiped my hands on my blue apron and ran outside to greet the returnees. Feiga and the children stood by my side. Tired and exhausted men dragged their feet across the dirt roads. Their faces had not been shaved for a long time. Their uniforms hung off their shoulders. Some of them were wrapped in bandages, others aided by crutches. The humiliated look in their eyes said it all.

Romania did not win the war. In fact, the country was now mostly occupied by enemy forces, but under the peace agreements, it looked as if they had won. Romania, now called "Greater Romania," managed to add to its geographical territory Transylvania, Bukovina, Bessarabia, and southern Dubrova.

The war years made our financial life difficult. Most of Piatra Neamț's residents were farmers, who grew their own food and traded it in other towns. During the war, the shortage of food and crops was noticeable. People were forced to reduce their living expenses.

Sewing new clothes or repairing hats became a luxury and Feiga was left with almost no income. The printing house where Tata worked had to cut down on expenses and a large number of the workers were sent back home, including him.

Somehow, we survived. The money Gisela and Victor sent helped us get through the cold winter months. Now, at the end of the war, we could breathe again and look forward to the future.

There was another reason that gave us hope. With the geographical territories added to Romania after the war, there were also big Jewish communities. There were now close to 700,000 Jews in Romania, three times what they had been before the war. According to the peace agreement between the warring countries, Romania was obliged to give minorities equal civil status.

Feiga and I, along with our children, continued to live in the house we grew up in. Aurica, my daughter, recently turned twelve and my son, Adrian, was now ten. They attended school in town, and played with the other students by the river, just as I once did with my siblings.

After Moshe's death, Feiga remained a widower for a while. Together, with Tata's help, we raised our six children. Occasionally, Mr. Fainaru knocked on our door with some requests for Feiga's hand in marriage. Most of the requests were from older widowers, who were looking for a woman to care for their children. Feiga rejected them all. Her Zionist dream unforgotten, she hoped that, one day, her dream of living in the land of Israel would come true. She feared marrying another man would prevent her from doing so.

However, among the soldiers who returned home, there was one prisoner of war, named Nicolai Slavitz. He had a dreamy look in his eyes. Feiga, like the other girls in town, was intrigued by him and his stories. "I saw a magic world," he said one night, as they sat on the riverside.

The liberated prisoner of war, Nicolai (or nicknamed by his friends, Nicu), was born in a small rural town in the region of Bessarabia. He had joined the Romanian army shortly before the outbreak of World War I. As an only child to poor hardworking farmers, he found refuge in climbing trees, waiting for someone to search for him. Since his parents were immigrants, he was fluent in Russian, French, and Romanian.

When the war broke out, he was sent on an intelligence mission with his unit to Belgium. When they arrived closer to the target, Nicu and his team learned that it had been a trap—the Germans were looking for them. His team fled. Nicu climbed and found refuge at the top of a thick tree. He remained there until the barks of the German Shepherd dogs ceased. After a few days, he realized that he was out of food and water. He had to leave his hiding place.

He climbed down from the tree and wandered without a clear direction for long days. He drank water from puddles of rain and ate carcasses of animals that he stumbled upon. He changed his clothes with those of the corpse of a dead farmer.

One morning before sunrise, he found himself in an agricultural town, bordering with France. He crossed the fence at twilight and passed the rest of the way on foot.

He managed to spend three days in Paris before being arrested. When he was arrested, he realized that if he declared that he was a Romanian soldier, the Romanian army would kill him for abandoning his post. But if he declared that he was born in Serbia and fled his town because of the war, he would only be imprisoned until the end of the war.

The three days he spent in Paris were engraved in his mind throughout his captivity. He was obsessed with the city and dreamed about living there.

Nicolai's stories fascinated everyone. From their small farming town, people could only imagine the charms of the big city. Feiga was captivated by his stories, both real and imagined. Nicu also became enchanted with Feiga and begged her to marry him. About a month later, Feiga agreed to his offer.

#

After Tata was forced to leave his job at the printing plant, his health began to deteriorate. The doctor determined it was a case of acute glaucoma, with no treatment. "Within a few weeks, he will become completely blind," the doctor told us.

For hours, Tata sat by the kitchen window and stared outside, as if watching an invisible butterfly. Slowly, he began to sink into depression and refused to leave the house, even for a walk. Just a few months after his diagnosis, Tata returned his soul to the Creator of the world. In October 1920, we buried Tata next to his beloved wife, our Mama.

All of my siblings came together for our father's funeral. David came without Sophie, for she was unable to attend due to her obligation as a music teacher for children with special needs. She sent her condolences and her love to everyone.

After dinner, David talked at length about his work as a schoolteacher in Iași. Excitedly, he told us about the intelligence of his students, the proficiency they demonstrated and their love for Romanian literature and Romanian poetry. He described the beauty of Iași, the many people he had come to know, and the cultural and theater performances he and Sophie often attended.

David also told us about an argument he'd had with a friend. While David believed that every person should live as a free and equal citizen in any country in which he chooses to live, his friend Ludovic, a colleague from school, was much more nationalistic. Despite these arguments between the two men, the friendship between David and Ludovic grew close and deep.

Zilli and her husband Alexander came from Constanța to attend the funeral. The salty sea air seemed to better Zilli's health and her skin was no longer pale as before. Her cheeks were tanned and her blonde hair was short. She looked much more mature than when she had left. Pinku and Yuly, their two young children, played joyfully with their cousins. They happily talked about the beach where they spent their summer vacations, the horse carousel that spun with lights and made joyous music, and the ice cream they got to eat at the carnivals. Pinku said that when he grew up, he would like to be a dentist, just like his father. Yuly promised that she would grow up to be a famous artist.

The twin sisters also came with their husbands. Elvira, her husband Isaac and their one-year-old daughter Friddie rode down with Gisela and her husband Victor from Bucharest, to accompany Tata on his final journey.

After dinner, the men retired to the living room to smoke their pipes. The sisters gathered in the kitchen for tea and cookies, while the kids went outside to play.

"And what are your plans now, Rosa?" Elvira asked.

I shrugged.

"Now that Tata is gone, why should you stay here? Feiga lives with Nicu, Zilli and Alexander in Constanta, David and Sophie in Iași. Gisela and I are in Bucharest. Why should you stay here with the children by yourself?"

"She's right," Gisela said. "What will happen if, God forbid, you become ill and need help? Who will take care of you? Why don't you come and live with me and Victor in Bucharest? Our house is big enough and we will be happy to host you."

I thanked them for their concern. "I don't want to disturb your lives," I said.

"We would love for you to come live with us!" they exclaimed in unison.

Zilli interjected, "And Rosa, the distance between Constanța and Bucharest is relatively short. You can spend long weekends with us and all of the summer months. It is pleasant by the sea and the children can get together and play on the beach."

I bit my lip. I had to admit that the offer enticed me, but the fear of leaving my home stalled me. It was the only place I knew like the back of my hand.

"And besides," Gisela snuggled up and hugged my waist, "maybe you'll meet a nice man in the big city. You're still too young to remain a widow all your life."

I was quiet. I looked at my sisters' faces. Their concern touched my heart. I loved them and wanted to be near them. I also knew the kids would love to spend the long summer months by the shores of the black sea.

Yet I was terrified. How could I pack all my belongings into three small suitcases? All my memories into a wooden crate? How would I manage in the big and bustling city? Wouldn't I get lost?

A well-known Romanian proverb says: "The gypsy drowns fifteen miles before he decides to cross the river." I was not a gypsy. I took a deep breath and decided to jump in and swim.

A few days later, my children and I made our way to the train station. Tears rolled down my cheeks as I watched my childhood home vanish behind me. I took a deep breath and pressed my handkerchief to my head. "We'll meet again," I whispered and closed my eyes, rolling my mother's silver ring in my pocket.

CHAPTER TWELVE

Rosa, 1941, Iași

Rosa held her grandson, the smell of lilacs pressing in from outside. Tears streamed down the wrinkles on her cheeks, but she did not stop them. They landed like rain upon Yossi's head, spreading out across his black hair and disappearing.

He leapt off her lap and ran outside. When the door swung closed, she read David's letter again, denial soaking into every fold of her brain.

***

My dear sisters,

If you are reading this letter, then please allow me first to apologize. I am sorry for saying goodbye this way. I want you to know that I love you. Even though our journey together in this world has come to an end, I will wait for you forever, wherever I may be.

I want you to know that I'm not afraid to die. I lived my life to the fullest. I knew true love from my family and dearest friends. I was privileged to see the beauty of nature, a world rich in birdsong, the morning dew, the blossom of the trees, the flow of the river, children's laughter. I couldn't ask for a more beautiful life.

I have always believed in the righteousness of the path we have followed. From a young age, I learned to put my trust in the hands of God, to appreciate my life journey and embrace my fate as it was set out for me. I don't know how my destiny will be determined here, whether a bullet will pierce my head or if I will be buried alive. I just know that I will not see the morning light.

I should have known, should have told you all sooner. Or left Iaşi. But I couldn't, for it is my home.

It all started the day I was fired. They did not even let me say goodbye to my dear students. I thought it was temporary, because of the war. I thought I would be reunited with my beloved classroom shortly after. Sophie's sad eyes told me she did not share my hope, but I still prayed for it.

Then, yesterday morning, a sharp whistle cut through the silence. Sophie was the first to realize. She was always the first. I naively thought it was just a squeaky truck or a gas balloon that had exploded. Sophie already knew. She sat in the living room, hands folded in her lap, as if waiting for the visitors.

And they came. So many. Romanian and German soldiers, Legionnaires, members of the Romanian Special Intelligence Service, police, and masses of residents. They banged on the doors, and when we answered, they yelled at us to go outside.

We were told to bring nothing but our ID cards.

It was hot, like most days in June, and so we hurried to dress the girls in comfortable clothes. We locked the door behind us. They were all waiting for us in the street. They ordered us to lower our heads and join the convoy of "dirty Jews" walking in lines. The girls were scared and Rachel, who is not yet four years old, started to cry, clinging to Sophie. I saw Sophie's desperate look while she held our daughters, as if she were already saying goodbye. Liliana, who just turned ten, hugged her sister Berta and tried to comfort her. I held Adela in my arms as we walked with the other Jews of Iaşi.

My heart pounded, and I could feel my pulse throughout my body. Thoughts kept running through my head. I was sweating under the long-sleeved jacket I had insisted on wearing. I proudly attached the medal I received during the Great War to the jacket, hoping that this medal would save us.

I was wrong.

Although the soldiers forbade us from looking up, I occasionally sneaked a quick look around and saw the ruins of the shops that once adorned our streets. Shattered glass covered the ground, huge swastikas were spray-painted in red across the businesses. Corpses piled up on the side of the road.

But what surprised me most were the people who joined the riots. Not only soldiers and Romanian policemen screamed and beat us, but also regular civilians. I recognized our neighbors and acquaintances, even some of my colleagues from school. My students were there too. Some of my best students, and some of the least able, were there among the angry crowd. I thought, how can this be?

After a thirty-minute walk, we reached the courtyard of the Kastura building, where most of the police were waiting. I was confused as to why we were coming to the police station, since this building was supposed to provide protection for all law-abiding citizens. We are decent citizens, never breaking the law. We have contributed to Romanian society; we have participated in the city's charity events and donated our hard-earned money many times. I fought in The Great War for the defense of Romania and was injured, an injury I have been dragging since then. Do we have no value at all? Were my contributions erased, as if I never existed?

I cannot begin to tell you the horrors we witnessed when we entered the Kastura. My mind refuses to remember, and my hands refuse to transcribe. All I can say is that the shootings did not stop; fellow Jews were screaming, bleeding, falling to the ground. My family rushed to hide, to find shelter, but the building doors were locked. We were helpless. All of a sudden, I felt a firm hand grabbing my arm and pulling me away from the massacre.

"Follow me," he ordered. "Now."

The man's voice was familiar, and I looked up towards him. Ludovic, my old friend, was holding my arm tightly.

"We'll survive," he assured.

"Ludovic? You're not even a Jew."

"I'm here for you," he replied.

I was able to drag Sophie and the girls away, following Ludovic's steps. He led us down a dark staircase into a tunnel to a hiding spot. It was stinking and overflowing with sewage. As we crawled, we barely breathed. My daughters cried for fresh air.

After a few minutes, which seemed like an eternity, we found ourselves crammed into a concrete shelter. Rats surrounded us, squeaking and making noises. I wanted to cry, I wanted to scream, "What's going on? It's not fair!" But I kept quiet. The girls hugged me as Sophie gripped my hand. God only knows where they got their courage.

We waited there. Shortly after midnight, Ludovic signaled for us to follow him again. After an unknown amount of time, we emerged from the sewers. I don't know how, but we were finally free. Looking around, we realized we were not far from our apartment. I sighed with relief, holding the girls closer to me.

Ludovic led us to our apartment. "It's all over now. You'll be safe," he promised.

"Ludovic," I said, my eyes filled with tears. I wanted to hug him, tell him how much I appreciated him risking his life for us.

"No... please." His eyes filled with tears. "It's all my fault. I knew about it... They told me last night... I thought it could never happen in such a progressive city like our Iași. I was so naive. I thought they were lying, making it up, that it couldn't be," he sobbed. "Why didn't I do something? Why didn't I stop it before?" His shoulders were shaking, his knees trembled, and he fell to his knees.

"Ludovic." I hugged his shoulders, trying to comfort him. "You saved me; you saved my family. I'll be grateful for you forever."

"No," he said, looking up at me. "I could have done more. I should have done more," he wept bitterly, "and now, all the Jews in the city are dead. Families, children, all of them!"

I led us into our apartment. We quickly realized that it had been looted. Our personal belongings were scattered or gone, the windows shattered, and glass covered the floor. We found our bedrooms shredded apart, but we collapsed quickly on the mattresses anyway to sleep.

We awoke the next morning to dreaded knocks on the door again. I went to the door and found Mr. Anton Andrei and his team of soldiers with guns and batons slapping in their hands. Mr. Andrei asked how we had managed to escape the police station yesterday, but I refused to answer. So did my family, my incredibly brave daughters and wife.

He ordered us to pack one suitcase individually for each passenger.

"You'll get on the train in half an hour," he said. "We'll make sure you get there safely."

Mr. Anton and his soldiers cruelly laughed, making my ears sting.

I appealed to his good and compassionate heart. After all, Mr. Anton was not just a policeman. His two sons, both very talented students, frequented my classes for years.

"Mr. Anton. Please."

Mr. Anton coughed and ran a hand through his thinning hair.

"Mr. Anton," I pleaded, "we have known each other for years, and you know how much I have done for our community. Will you find it in your heart to protect me? My family? Please, have mercy on us."

"Difficult dilemma," he hummed.

I closed my eyes tightly. My lips began to murmur a soft prayer. "Hear O Israel..." I whispered, hoping for it to find its way into Mr. Anton's merciful heart.

"You know what," said Mr. Anton. "Mr. Postelnic, you are an intellectual, right? A man who considers himself smart. So, I will leave

the choice up to you." He cleared his throat. "You understand, we must cut off the rotten branches. God forbid more moldy fruit would grow, right?" He paused for a moment. "Send your daughters to the train, now, without hesitation. My staff and I will make sure they arrive safely. You and your wife may stay here. I will make sure you get back to your job in school and continue to educate our pure-blood next generation. You and your wife Sophie will not be harmed."

I stared at him in disbelief. Tears flowed down my cheeks, dripping onto my shirt. Without a word, I turned back into the apartment. Sophie, having overheard the conversation, wrapped me in her arms.

We started packing our suitcases with some personal belongings. I proudly wore my medal for the very last time.

I asked for a moment to write this last letter.

I'm sending all my love to you, my dear sisters. I feel honored that I had the pleasure of living by your side.

I hope this letter finds its way to you. Mysterious are the ways of the universe.

With all my heart,

David

***

Rosa crumpled the letter in her fist and walked to the window to watch Yossi play. He was about the age of David's youngest daughter. A knot tied up in her gut. Her throat clenched as tears streamed softly down her face.

Her son Adrian had returned from work early with this letter, having received it from one of the partners at his firm. It had somehow made its way to Bucharest and found Rosa here. She cursed the letter and the violence befalling her family. She thought since they had survived the Bucharest pogroms earlier that year, everything would be alright. She was wrong. And now, her brother and his family had perished in the Iași massacre.

After a few moments, Yossi came back in. She quickly got herself together. As she made him a snack, she sent a prayer to her brother and his family, knowing that one day they would meet again in Heaven.

David proudly wearing his medal of honor

Sophie and David, last known photo (1940)

CHAPTER THIRTEEN

The Rosenthal family, 1948, Bucharest

By early 1944, Romania ran into a huge economic crisis, resulting from the high expenses incurred from fighting in World War II. Romania was a loyal ally of Nazi Germany and sent its best men to fight alongside the Axis powers. In August 1944 however, Romanian civilians were fed up with the war and exhausted by the disgraceful economic situation. They demanded change.

Under the leadership of King Mihai[22], the Romanian army and Romanian opposition forces overthrew the Prime Minister, Ion Antonescu. Romania's best troops joined the United States and the Allies.

At the end of the war, the Romanian geographical territories in Serbia and northern Bukovina became a part of the Soviet Union. King Mihai was deposed and exiled to Switzerland, and Romania became a Republica Populară Română (communist republic) under the Soviet Union and its leader, Joseph Stalin.

In 1948, Gheorghe Gheorghiu-Dej was declared the leader of the communist-Romanian state.

In May of the same year, David Ben-Gurion declared the establishment of the State of Israel, the independent national home for the Jewish people. Joy from Jews was heard around the world.

The Rosenthal family, whose dream of Zionism had been ingrained in Aurel since childhood, began to search for certificates that would allow them to "establish a Jewish home in the Land of Israel," as the Israeli Declaration said.

On his first visit to the Jewish National Fund offices in Bucharest, Aurel was given a Hebrew name: Aharon. His wife's name was changed from Aurica to the Hebrew name Golda. Even then, however, Aurel realized that, in order to make the journey to Israel, he would need a huge sum of money to bribe the Romanian officials. They would also need funds to get on a ship to Israel, hopefully from Constanța.

About a week after his visit to the Jewish National Fund's offices in Bucharest, a raid was carried out on the offices. Many documents were confiscated, the organization's activists were arrested, and the offices were closed. For now, Aurel had to shelve his dream.

Aurica was not an ardent partner in her husband's Zionist plans. Rosa's eyesight was deteriorating, and Aurica had turned all her attention to her mother; she took charge of her mother's catering business, while also raising Yossi to be a respectable Jewish Romanian boy.

The doctor determined that Rosa's blurry vision was caused by acute glaucoma, which had also plagued her father. Her eyesight would deteriorate soon to almost complete blindness. "She will need a lot of help," the doctor advised the family.

Aurel was not the only one who dreamed of returning to the land of milk and honey. Rosa's sister, Feiga, gave Adrian her books on Zionist poetry, which had accompanied her for most of her life. She managed to transfer her love of Zionism not only to her own children, but to Rosa's children as well. Nicu, her second husband, refused to give up on his dreams to live in Paris and so the couple decided to part ways. One day, in late 1949, a short letter arrived in Rosa's mailbox. The letter said:

My dear sister Rosa,

At last, I am happy! I am a Zionist now, for all intents and purposes. After a difficult sea voyage, we reached the shores of the Land of Israel. I have no words to describe the happiness I felt when the ship docked, off the coast of Haifa. I hugged myself and my children and tears of joy flowed down my cheeks. We were housed in a small hut and given some hot food. I'm not complaining. Easy days do not await me here, I know. Embrace everyone in my name.

All my love,

Feiga

#

Eight years had passed since Friddie's disappearance, and her parents, Elvira and Isaac, were heartbroken. They knocked on every door, asking, begging, pleading for any information about their beloved daughter. The turmoil of the communist regime and the pronounced resentment against the Jews, although not declared as official anti-Semitism, did not benefit the unfortunate parents.

One day, when poor Isaac was on his way to the Government Office for Civil Affairs, he walked in on a conversation he should not have heard.

"What does this Jew want again?" one clerk asked his officemate when he saw Isaac walking up the concrete stairs slowly. Isaac gasped heavily and a desperate look came across his eyes. His skin was pale and his hair completely white.

"I have no idea." The other clerk shrugged. "He's probably still looking for his daughter."

"Isn't he worn out by now?" the first one asked. "She's probably just another one of those Jewish prostitutes, who died a long time ago and were buried in anonymous graves."

"Who knows?" The first clerk laughed. "And who cares?"

Isaac, who had arrived at the door, heard their conversation and his eyes filled with tears. Without a word, he turned around and, with heavy steps, left the building.

The parents saved every penny to hire private investigators, but they returned empty-handed. Friddie's name was not in any official document. They realized that Friddie's fate was lost to them forever.

A few weeks later, in early February 1949, Isaac's heart stopped beating. When he closed his eyes for the very last time, a tear rolled down his cheeks, and with his last breath he cried, "Fridda."

With the death of her beloved husband and the disappearance of her only daughter, Elvira lost her sanity. For long hours, she would sit in a dark room, covered with a thick blanket she pulled over her head, mumbling vague words. Letting the darkness comfort her as it once had her daughter.

She refused to eat or talk to anyone. Her sisters, Gisela and Rosa, visited her day after day, but were unable to persuade Elvira to leave the room or try Rosa's delicacies.

In their sorrow, the sisters sought help. When a space finally became available in an asylum, Elvira was transferred to her new home. Her bed was placed by a large window, overlooking the street and blue skies. Elvira fell silent, and she never spoke again until her final day.

In 1949, under heavy pressure from Joseph Stalin, Romania was forced to fund a project to connect the Danube River to the Black Sea. The project aimed to shorten the naval voyage on the way to the Black Sea, draining swampy soils in Dobrogea and allowing a continuous passage from Moscow to Central Europe.

The Romanians, led by Prime Minister Gheorghe Gheorghiu-Dej, tried first to avoid the project, due to a lack of budget and suitable mechanical engineering equipment, but their claims were rejected outright by Stalin. Stalin promised that the Soviet Union would provide the appropriate equipment and funds if Romania provided the labor. The agreement to build the Danube-Black Sea Canal was signed in July 1949 and Romania began setting up labor camps to concentrate the workers. Many inmates found themselves integrated into these forced labor camps.

Friddie was among them.

CHAPTER FOURTEEN

Friddie, 1949, The Danube Canal Labor Camps

The prison cells filled up over the years. Sounds of sobs and screams became commonplace, echoing up and down the hallways. Whispers between prisoners took place underneath the shouts, deals being struck for basic necessities. No one came in with anything, so they could only make the worst of trades with the guards. They would give their captors golden teeth, or a moment alone with their bodies, in exchange for cigarettes, soap, or even an extra loaf of bread. Friddie had been there longer than the others and forgot what it meant to need anything. She only craved a pen and paper to write, as her escape. The nurses would bring these to her for free, only asking for Friddie to read them some of her poetry. For they were trapped in their own ways.

Detective Stalie arrived at Friddie's cell unexpectedly one afternoon, nine years into her captivity. She was about to complete a new poem. As soon as she noticed the unexpected visitor, she immediately stood up, shoving the paper into the mattress. The ink pen fell out of her hand and rolled across the ground, spinning around loudly like a broken toy.

"What do we have here?" sneered Detective Stalie, spotting the papers peeking out from the mattress.

Friddie's heart pounded against her ribs. She didn't say a word. She was afraid of what would come next. A slap in the face? Or something worse? Would he burn all her poetry, or question her about where she got her supplies? She knew that, no matter what she said, it would only complicate her situation. She stood there silently. She didn't dare meet his eye.

The detective pulled the papers from under the mattress and thumbed through them. "Instead of a spy, you have decided to become a poet?" He began reading one page, pacing slowly around her. He looked back up at her pale face. She could see evil sparks in his eyes. He stood very close to her, looking straight into her eyes. She could smell cigar smoke and whiskey on his tongue. His fingers fluttered around her neck and face. "You know," he whispered, "I also enjoy poetry occasionally, mostly while making love."

Her whole body stiffened at once. She felt vomit rise in her throat. She closed her eyes tightly. She didn't dare to move; her heart was pounding fast. He started laughing as if he had changed his mind and took a step back.

"What awaits you today is much worse than that, Mrs. Karl," he snarled. "I'll be a gentleman and give you a minute to get yourself together. When you're ready, come with me. And don't try anything stupid. Understood?" He pulled up his shirt to reveal a shining pistol pressed against his pale skin. Friddie didn't know why he bothered—he always kept it there.

Friddie's heart pounded. She wanted to ask where he was taking her, but she knew he would not tell her. Adrenaline poured through her veins from the detective's advances, and her ears pounded.

She didn't need a minute to get organized. Her only "property" was the pile of poems she had written. He gave her back the papers and, when he left the cell, she shoved them in her bra. She stepped out of her room and stood next to Detective Stalie quietly.

Detective Stalie glanced at her and motioned for her to follow. She walked behind him silently, down a dark corridor. Then they climbed steep stairs and walked down another dark corridor. The lights were dim, but Friddie could see more prison cells in this hallway, many more than when she had arrived so long ago. Hushed whispers followed her every step. She didn't dare to look up, but knew that many sad eyes were watching her. She could smell the despair in the hallways, a mixture of sour urine and stale bread, a mixed smell of misery and death.

After a few more minutes of walking, only their footsteps echoing against the walls, Detective Stalie stopped in front of a heavy iron door. He pulled out a large bundle of keys and opened the upper lock. He looked back and sneered. As he pushed the door open, it let out a screeching scream.

Bright sunlight poured into the darkness. Friddie covered her eyes with her elbow, crying out in surprise. The bright light burned her eyes and tears began to flow. She hadn't seen daylight for so long—since she'd first been taken. Her head was hammering from a sudden headache. She hid her face in the prisoner's gown she was wearing.

Detective Stalie burst out laughing. "Are the sun rays pleasant to your eyes?" he mocked. "Maybe you should write a poem about that."

He placed a heavy hand on her shoulders and pushed her firmly towards a military truck parked nearby. With her eyes still closed, Friddie groped her way up into the truck. She blindly felt around until she found a low wooden bench in the back. She sat down, continuing to protect her eyes with her arm.

"We had the pleasure of hosting you, Mrs. Fridda Karl. Good luck on your next adventure."

"Where am I going?" she asked.

"Just wait and see." He laughed again, the sound pounding against Friddie's ears. "You'll love it there." His terrible laugh haunted her for years to come, often coming to her in nightmares.

Slowly, Friddie opened her eyes. Everything was still blurry and painful. She saw soldiers surrounding the truck, holding weapons. She heard orders, commands, shouts. She felt the truck shake, as more prisoners were loaded in. They pushed her to the side as they took their places on the bench next to her. No prisoners dared to say anything, their eyes also covered with clothing or limbs, to protect them from the light.

A few minutes later, when the truck was full, two armed soldiers jumped in the back of the truck, to maintain order. A command was given, "Go!"

#

Close to 100,000 political prisoners worked on the construction of the canal, connecting the Danube River and the Black Sea. After the agreement between Romania and the Soviet Union was signed in July 1949, fourteen forced labor camps were built to house prisoners along the river. The labor camps were quickly filled with Romanian intellectuals, peasants who refused to give up their land, members of clergy, and political prisoners from jails throughout the country. About five to seven thousand prisoners were stationed in each camp.

The prisoners included people with various belief systems and backgrounds. In the camps, there were farmers who opposed collectivization; former activists of the National Peasants' Party, the Liberal National Party, and the Romanian Social Democratic Party, who opposed the current regime; Zionist Jews; and Orthodox and Catholic priests. No wonder canal labor camps were known as the "graveyard of the Romanian bourgeoisie," becoming the place to eliminate undesirable social classes.

The main labor camp was called Poarta Albă, where the number of prisoners at the camp was doubled, more than in any other camp.

Friddie was brought to that camp.

#

The sanitary conditions in the labor camps were terrible and the horrible weather made life miserable. During hot summer days, the prisoners had to deal with diseases such as Tuberculosis, typhoid and dysentery, caused by working next to swamps, as well as insects like mosquitoes. In winter, the camps were covered with heavy piles of snow that buried tired prisoners underneath them. Prisoners often peed on their hands to keep themselves warm.

The daily ration was minimal. Each prisoner was given one thin slice of bread in the morning. For dinner, they received a cup of muddy soup with another thin slice of bread. Often prisoners hunted mice and insects for protein. Proper medical care was not available and, if a prisoner became ill, they would likely perish.

Each worker was assigned a daily work quota of digging or clearing stones. If a prisoner did not complete the quota set for them, they would spend the night in a dank cell. Workers were equipped with simple hand-digging tools, such as a hoe, a pitchfork, and a wheelbarrow for moving piles of stones and heavy rocks. In the winter, under large piles of snow, the soil was difficult to dig. As a result, the number of injuries increased, bleeding hands became a matter of routine, the grueling work caused physical and mental exhaustion, and, of course, diseases increased sickness and mortality.

Shortly after sunset, a loud whistle sound would be heard all over the camp. It was a signal for the prisoners to go back to their halls and rest before the next working day, which started at sunrise.

The prisoners slept side by side on long plank boards with thin mattresses. In the middle of the hall stood one metal bucket that was used by the prisoners to defecate. Every morning, they had to empty the bucket into a hole outside. The stench was overwhelming—Friddie was disturbed by how quickly she got used to it.

The large halls where they slept were so cold during the winter that prisoners would huddle next to each other, sitting up in order to maintain their body heat. Needless to say, not all inmates woke up in the morning. The corpses of those that froze overnight were thrown into the cistern.

The women's labor camps were separated from the men's by electric fences and high stone walls. "Whoever dares to approach the wall will be shot to death," the prisoners were warned on the first day they arrived at the camp. Armed guards constantly roamed the camps and kept order. At times, when guards wished for some sexual entertainment, they did not hesitate to visit the women's hall and do as they pleased.

A prisoner who violated curfew was immediately executed. Prisoners trying to escape from the camp were shot by the guards in the towers or eaten by wolves roaming outside the fence. Once, several prisoners tried to pretend to be dead and escape through an improvised coffin. The camp commander wanted to confirm their deaths and stuck an iron handlebar through their hearts. Their bodies were thrown into a hole and set on fire.

It is for that reason that the Danube Canal was nicknamed the "Death Canal" (Canalul morții).

#

There, in the abyss of despair, in those moments when everything seems lost, when hopelessness overwhelmed, where disaster was considered normal, and all hope seemed abandoned… It was there, at that moment, that a small ray of light was revealed.

One night, a few weeks after Friddie's arrival at the labor camp, she lay on a makeshift bed, writing poetry by candlelight. Looking up for a moment to think, she saw a strange silhouette pass by the door.

It was a shadow with a long tail flicking upwards. It was evening, and the night curfew was about to begin in a couple of minutes.

At first, she thought her eyes were deceiving her. She rubbed them. Am I going crazy? she whispered to herself. Can it be? Is it really... a cat?

Friddie closed her eyes tightly and opened them once again.

"No, that can't be..." she murmured.

A few days later, the shadow reappeared. Friddie was lying on a mattress again, letting her aching bones rest. The silhouette with a long tail emerged by the doorway and then disappeared.

"Do you see that?" she asked another prisoner.

"Sure," she said.

"Really? Do you see that cat too?"

The other prisoner burst out laughing. "She went crazy." She pointed at Friddie. The other prisoners in the room joined her cackling.

"Poor woman, we will all lose our minds here," said one of the girls, sending Friddie a merciful look.

Friddie shrugged and laid her head on the wooden board that served as her bed.

But when the incident repeated itself for the third time, Friddie could no longer resist and hurried after the creature.

"Where are you going, crazy?" one of the girls in the room shouted. "The curfew is about to begin. If you are not in bed, they will shoot you or throw you into the dungeon. You'll get all of us in trouble."

Friddie tiptoed after the tail. As she got closer, she was convinced she was not hallucinating. It was a small, gray cat with shining eyes that occasionally stopped and let out a soft mewl. She had no doubt that the cat was just as scared as she was.

"Psss..." she whispered to the cat. "Come to me... Please come closer... Do not be afraid. I want to feel your fur... Psss..."

The cat peered back at her, and then darted off to the wall that separated the men's and women's camps. Friddie stopped in her tracks, afraid to approach the wall. Yet the cat refused to slow down. Occasionally, it looked back to make sure Friddie was following, and so she did. Suddenly, it leapt over the wall, passed through the barbed fence, and disappeared.

"Psss... Where are you?" Friddie whispered. "Please come back!"

Friddie froze. On the other side of the wall, she heard the voice of a man whispering, "Psssss... Cat, cat... Where are you? Come to me. I will give you food..."

Friddie was silent. Any communication between men and women was strictly forbidden. She knew that. Still, her curiosity grew.

"I'm sorry," Friddie whispered to the wall. "Maybe you happened to see a cat passing by here?" She was afraid. Maybe she was getting herself in trouble. She chided herself, imagining this stranger reporting her to the guards.

After a moment, the voice reemerged from the other side. "I swear, I thought I was going crazy. Did you also see a cat? And…" He hesitated. "Who are you? My name is Mircea."

"My name is Friddie," she whispered. "I'm not a guard. I'm a prisoner too and I so wanted to hug the cat... stroke his fur."

"Me too." He let out a sigh. "I'm sorry."

She pressed her hand against the wall.

A strong loud whistle sounded.

"I have to go," Mircea whispered. Friddie could hear footsteps rapidly retreating, and she too ran back to her stiff mattress. That night, she dreamed of cats and a deep voice telling her that everything would be fine.

CHAPTER FIFTEEN

Mircea, 1909, The Royal Palace, Bucharest

Mircea was born on a cold winter night in January 1909. His mother, who had already buried three babies previously, didn't expect a miracle this time either. But Mircea was a healthy, chubby baby. He cried and howled for hours on end. The only thing that comforted him was breastfeeding, latching onto his mother's breast and not letting go. The baby's hunger was insatiable, and his mother, though tired and exhausted, was unparalleled in her happiness.

Mircea's father witnessed his son's birth, though he was often away from home, serving as the town's sole physician. Mircea's father, Dr. Choiboteru, made sure to visit every patient, those who were taking their first breath and those who were taking their last. His patients included both the poor and wealthy.

He was not only a talented and wise doctor, but also a compassionate one. He took care of the mental state of his patients, as well as their physical condition. His reputation as the good doctor spread far and wide. Residents from nearby towns and distant villages often visited his home, bringing their patients to him by carriage. If they could not come to him, he would willingly go to their homes

Mircea grew up full of joyful memories. Smells of delicacies and aromas rose from the large kitchen, where his mother and the maids cooked meals for the family and guests, who were often invited to join them for dinner. Dr. Choiboteru loved to tell stories about his work and the interesting people he met along the way. He would always end his stories with a wise message, emphasizing the connection between body and soul. He often thanked God for giving him the ability to help other human beings.

Mircea fondly remembered attending church on Sundays. He was proud to hold his father's hand. He could feel the respect and admiration surrounding his family. Hearing his father's voice singing in church fascinated him.

When Mircea was ten years old, a telegram arrived at the Choiboteru household. The telegram said that Dr. Choiboteru must report to the Presidential King's Palace immediately, to fulfill his role as the head of the royal medical staff. For his trouble, he would receive a one-time payment that guaranteed his service for life. He would be allowed to visit his family every couple of weeks when the king or other members of the royal court did not require his services.

The evening he was summoned, Mircea's father packed his clothes, kissed his family goodbye, and got into the carriage that drove him to his new home.

King Ferdinand and his wife, Princess Maria of Edinburgh, did not often socialize in the palace. They rarely held official receptions at the royal palace, but when they did, senior Romanian government officials were invited, including the senior medical team.

For the most part, however, the royal couple often locked themselves in their rooms separately. King Ferdinand loved his country and the Romanian people. He often worked for his citizens. He believed in their free will, in liberalization and equality of rights.

The royal couple had six children, three sons and three daughters. Prince Carol, who was the eldest son, was appointed heir apparent and the candidate to inherit his father's role upon his death. But Carol II had plans of his own.

As a child, Carol II realized that he was destined to inherit his father's responsibilities. His upbringing was overly rigorous. As soon as Carol turned four years old, private tutors were assigned to him, whose job was to make sure that the toddler behaved properly as the royal son. Carol had to learn foreign languages, such as French, Latin, and German; memorize historical facts and important events; master extensive geographical skills; and have a knowledge of economics and an appropriate cultural-literary background. He was forbidden to play and waste time in idleness or social life. Instead, he was required to attend state events, and behave as expected of a future king.

Carol II hated his teachers, hated the expectations placed on him, and longed to rebel and be free. His brothers and sisters, who were not in line for the throne, could play as they pleased. Carol envied and resented them for it. In 1914, when Carol was twenty-one years old, he fled the palace to Odessa and married his lover, Zizi Lambrino, despite the opposition of his father.

A few years later, a child was born to the couple. Carol returned to the palace shortly after the birth, refusing to acknowledge the child as his.

When Carol II returned to the palace, his father, King Ferdinand, immediately ordered the annulment of his son's marriage to Zizi, on the grounds that the marriage was illegal. He expelled his son from the palace to the convent.

In 1921, Carol II met Elena, Princess of Greece and Denmark. By order of his parents, he married her. In October that year, their only son, Mihai, was born.

#

Prince Carol found a sympathetic ear in his personal physician, Dr. Choiboteru. Dr. Choiboteru, who believed that bodily ailments were directly related to mental illness, made sure to devote his time and energy to the young man. Prince Carol obviously needed his doctor's support. Dr. Choiboteru witnessed the unrealistic demands on the young prince and the challenges that King Ferdinand imposed on his eldest son. As such, a close and personal relationship developed between the two, and Carol trusted his doctor more than anyone else in life.

Prince Carol asked the doctor to stay as close to the palace as possible, so when he learned of the doctor's wife and son waiting for his return, he invited the doctor's family to live in the palace. When Mircea turned thirteen, he and his mother moved to the royal palace to be with Mircea's father.

The friendship between Prince Carol and the doctor was not the only close bond that was formed in the palace. Mihai, the son of Prince Carol and Elena, was a uniquely curious toddler. He adopted Mircea as his older brother. Mircea always wanted a younger brother and embraced the toddler into his heart. He was happy to play with him, under the close supervision of the nannies, of course.

In 1925, Prince Carol announced that he was officially relinquishing his right to reign and transferred the right to his son Mihai, who just turned four. Two years later, in 1927, when Ferdinand I died, Mihai was crowned King of Romania. Due to his young age, a committee was appointed for him, to act on behalf of the king. Among the unofficial advisers of King Mihai were Mircea and Dr. Choiboteru.

In 1930, when King Mihai was nine years old, his father Carol II returned to the palace and retook his role as king of Romania.

King Carol II reigned from 1930 to 1940. King Carol II, unlike his father, needed love and authority to strengthen his power. In 1938, the Romanian people strongly opposed him. So, he decided to abolish the existing government and appoint under him a ruling, fascist party called the National Renaissance Front. He appointed General Ion Antonescu, who was an ardent supporter of Hitler and responsible for the Iași pogrom, to be the head of government.

In September 1940, General Ion Antonescu removed King Carol II from the palace and appointed his son Mihai as the official king of Romania again. King Carol fled to Portugal in a train carrying twelve carriages full of wealth, jewelry, diamonds, famous art, and other looted treasures. He later married his mistress, Magda Lupescu. He remained in Portugal until 1953, where he died of cancer.

At the age of eighteen, Mihai became the King of Romania for the second time. This time, he officially appointed a special adviser, his older "brother" Mircea.

King Mihai ruled during World War II, during the pro-Nazi regime under the official leadership of dictator Ion Antonescu, whom he loathed with every vein of his soul. King Mihai hated the Nazi administration and stayed away from any meeting with representatives of the anti-Semitic regime. More than once, he stormed into Mircea's office, slammed the door behind him, and ranted about the state of the country.

On September 1, 1944, King Mihai's dream finally came true. With the help of the king's loyal advisers and the support of politicians from Allied countries, the royal palace guards finally imprisoned Ion Antonescu. Mihai's joy knew no bounds when he handed over Ion Antonescu to the leaders of the communist regime. They sentenced Antonescu to death for the war crimes he had committed and for the death of innocent civilians.

Mihai served as the King of Romania under the communist regime for two more years, but avoided cooperating with the pro-

Soviet government. In 1947, he traveled to London to attend the wedding of his cousin Princess Elizabeth II to Prince Philip, Duke of Edinburgh. Upon his return to Romania, the Romanian Communist Prime Minister ordered him to sign a document willingly for his removal from office and the end of the monarchy in Romania. Mihai was given twenty-four hours to leave the country.

The king begged Mircea and Dr. Choiboteru to accompany him and live in peace in exile. He promised that his possessions and jewelry would be enough to keep everyone alive for many years to come. Some of his advisers agreed to accompany him into exile.

"Please, come with me," Mihai begged Mircea. "I cannot ensure your safety if you stay."

"My father would never leave his patients," said Mircea. "They need him, and he would never let them down. Besides, it's the only place he knows. That we know."

"Save yourself," Mihai pleaded. "I don't know what's going to happen here after I'm gone. They will come after anyone who was associated with the royal palace."

"I'm sorry," Mircea said, his voice full of emotion. "How can I abandon my parents? I'm their only son. Maybe if I stay here, I'll be able to change the administration's mind about my father."

"Please. I need you. You are my only brother. You are the only one I trust. If you come with me, I can protect you."

"I'm sorry," said Mircea.

They embraced, not knowing it would be the last time they would see each other.

"We'll meet again," the fallen king promised. "I will ask them to spare you the harsh punishment they have in mind." He gripped Mircea's hands. "The Communists won't rule Romania forever."

#

A few hours after Mihai fled the palace, regime soldiers broke in and arrested everyone who had faithfully served the king. Among them were Dr. Choiboteru and his son, Mircea. Mircea's mother had disappeared, and he did not hear from her again for many years.

Mircea's father felt a sharp pain in his heart while being arrested. His son Mircea was by his side and encouraged him to hope and believe that they would soon be set free.

The court decided the fate of the two men. "You have served and collaborated with the monarchical government. You will be imprisoned indefinitely," the judge declared.

In jail, Mircea was pacing back and forth, trying to come up with a way to plead their case. He heard a choked breath in the corner where his father sat. He turned and watched his father taking his last breath. By the time Mircea reached his father, he was dead.

After his case bounced around in the courts for a couple of years, Mircea was sentenced to work in Romania as an indentured servant. He was handcuffed and loaded onto a military truck, similar to the one that transported Friddie. The doors to the truck opened, and he was pushed forward by the other prisoners into the Danube Canal labor camp called Poarta Albă.

CHAPTER SIXTEEN

Friddie and Mircea, 1950, Poarta Albă - Behind the Stone Wall

The love story between Friddie and Mircea bloomed like most love stories, except for a couple of crucial details. The brief conversations between the couple took place through the high stone wall, under constant dread of the whistle announcing curfew hours. They could not see the sparks in the other's eyes while staring at the stone wall. Their only solace was pressing their foreheads against the rough granite, tracing the minerals and pretending to feel the body warmth of the other person.

Every night, the couple approached the exact same spot behind the stone wall, where the cat silhouette was last seen. Slowly, over brief encounters, they got to know each other. Friddie was a decade younger than Mircea, but he felt that she was more mature and down-to-earth than any woman he had ever met.

The couple never promised to meet the next day. Neither of them knew if they would survive to see another evening or hear the morning whistles. They also never talked about their future; instead, they shared stories of their past.

Only once Mircea dared ask how Friddie came to be in this prison camp. After a long pause, Friddie softly replied, "I married the wrong man, in the wrong place, at the wrong time."

They remained still, foreheads pressed against the cool stone. "How did you end up here?" Friddie whispered.

"I am the son of a wonderful man, who served the wrong people, at the wrong place, at the wrong time," Mircea replied.

In only one sentence, they had summarized their entire lives.

Short conversations, stolen moments, and silence made them closer.

"I'm afraid one day you'll see what I look like and be disappointed," said Friddie one evening, her hand tracing the scars and wrinkles on her face.

"I'd never," Mircea promised. "Your soul is so beautiful. I will never let your outward appearance deceive me." He paused, a smile growing on his face. "Perhaps you have scars, my love, but nothing will ever compare to the poetry inside you."

Three years after the approval for the Danube Canal excavation project was given, the Romanians realized the project was about to fail. The prisoners, who weren't skilled in excavation work, didn't progress at the expected pace. They quickly ran out of appropriate equipment, the money allocated for the project was depleted, and the engineering plans were found to be faulty. The project reached a dead end. The communist regime sought who to blame. They even claimed that a deliberate hand intentionally caused the project to fail.

Heavy pressure was exerted on the prisoners to increase the pace of their work. The excavation quota for each prisoner was doubled. A prisoner who did not meet the daily quota was thrown into a dungeon or beaten. Punishments were given out nonstop. Prisoners' sleeping hours were cut and food rations reduced. They were beaten, unless they worked faster. More prisoners perished quickly now, both in their sleep and while working.

Arguments broke out among the officers, blaming each other, accusing their commanders and everyone around them. Senior command visited the camps more often, to learn why the work was not progressing at the required pace, often blaming the camp commanders. The pressure was felt everywhere.

Friddie and Mircea could seldom meet. They knew that, if they were caught, they would be killed.

One day, during a senior commander's visit, Mircea suddenly noticed a familiar face. At first, he thought his eyes were deceiving him. The heat and hard physical work sometimes caused Mircea to hallucinate. But this time, Mircea also had a strange feeling. Although the prisoners were ordered not to look directly at the commanders, this time Mircea dared. As the senior commander walked by the place where Mircea knelt in a pit, he raised his head and stared straight into the commander's eyes. The commander looked confused, then angry, his face becoming red. He was about to pull out his gun and teach the rude prisoner a lesson, when a spark suddenly ignited in his eyes. It was clear they had met before. The senior commander frowned and continued on his way. Mircea went back to work.

The next day, Mircea was called to the camp commander's room. The order was given without any explanation. "Tomorrow, at 5:30 a.m., you will report to the main work gate. A military vehicle will be waiting for you. You will be handcuffed. Do not dare to resist or ask questions or you will be shot. Understood?"

Mircea nodded and hurried to get away.

He eagerly awaited his meeting with Friddie that night. After waiting for over an hour, he heard her footsteps approaching the wall. As soon as they stopped, he whispered, "I'm leaving." She was silent. "I don't know where I am being taken. I think it has to do with the commander's visit. I remember him. He was a senior officer among the royal guard. He was the first to abandon the king's services and revolt." Mircea pressed his hand against the wall, his throat tightening. "I don't know what will happen to me." He heard Friddie sobbing on the other side of the wall. "Don't worry, my love," he promised, "I will find a way to get back to you, living or dead."

#

The next morning, Mircea showed up at the camp gates at the designated time. His heart was pounding.

"Are you Mr. Choiboteru?" the officer asked.

Mircea nodded.

The officer handcuffed both his hands and feet with long, heavy chains. "Follow me," he commanded.

They walked quietly. A military van awaited them. Mircea climbed in and found a seat in the back. Two officers jumped in and took their seats in the front. They were both armed. The vehicle doors closed.

"Put it on your head," one officer said and handed Mircea a black head cover. It had a strong smell, like almonds. He became dizzy instantly. He closed his eyes and covered his head with the black bag. From a distance, he heard the heavy iron gates closing behind them in a horrible shriek as the van pulled away. His breathing became heavy and deep, his vision swimming. As he was about to black out, his lips whispered soundlessly, "Goodbye, Friddie, my love. Goodbye."

#

In March 1953, Stalin died. Soon after, the Romanian government decided to stop the excavation of the Danube Canal. Eight people, who were considered the leaders of the Danube Excavation Project, were arrested by the Securitate, Romania's secret police, and charged with intentional sabotage of the project. Using violence, torture, and threats, the defendants were forced to sign a letter of confession.

Some of the prisoners were transferred to other labor camps in northern Dobroja, under similar conditions. Some prisoners were sent back to jail. A small group of political prisoners were released. Among them was Friddie.

It was a bright Sunday morning, August 9, 1953, when the gates of the camp opened. Thirteen women, including Friddie, were ordered to march forward. "Get out of here," soldiers shouted at them. "But remember! One word against our great leaders and you will be back here before you have time to make babies," the guards shouted.

The prisoners lowered their eyes to the ground and said nothing. "Leave now! 1, 2, 3… March!"

With hesitant steps, the women crossed through the gate. They knew that even the smallest mistake would cost them their life. The metal gates closed behind them with a shriek. The thirteen women were lost. They looked at each other hopelessly, paralyzed.

Friddie stood there, among them, for a long time. She was confused. Although physically she was free, in her mind, she was still behind the bars. What do I do now? Where do I go? She froze in place. She heard running noises and looked back. A group of prisoners rushed behind the locked gate to receive their daily ration of bread.

Run, a voice shouted inside her head. Go! Now! Thirteen years in prison. You are free at last! cried the voice. She found a rock close to the gate and sat down, lost in her thoughts. Her legs folded beneath her. She clasped the pieces of poetry she had managed to save throughout the years to her bare stomach.

Go home, Friddie, go back to your family, the voice whispered deep inside her. Friddie's eyes began to water. Mom, Dad, Mircea... Where will I find you...?

A black car creaked up next to her. A handsome man wearing a black suit and a red tie came out of the driver's seat. His eyes were smiling. Friddie looked into his eyes and knew.

"Come with me," he whispered and held out his hand toward her. "I was waiting for you."

CHAPTER SEVENTEEN

The Rosenthal Family, 1951, From Bucharest to Israel

In Spring 1951, the long-awaited certificates were finally received, and Aurel Rosenthal breathed a sigh of relief. His dreams were about to come true. Within a few days, their life would change for the better. They would finally board the *Transylvania* ship, which would take them to their homeland. To Israel.

Aurel and his family boarded the dilapidated ship in Constanța, which quickly became overcrowded. The sea raged the whole trip. Even through the sleepless nights, Aurel's desires were finally fulfilled. The dream for which he fought, struggled, and dragged his feet from office to office across Bucharest was finally here. It was about to come true.

Aurel had to battle with government officials and public representatives to get permission to leave Romania. But he also had to fight within his own family. Aurica, who usually supported his desires, tried to persuade him to shelve the dream, postpone this voyage, and remain in Bucharest, where she was accustomed to living.

He understood her concerns. She feared surviving the journey, the worries of getting to a new place, the adjustment to the difficult weather and unpredictable climate, adapting to a foreign country, learning a new language, while fighting for her family's daily survival. Above all, Aurica worried about Yossi. "How can the boy say goodbye to his friends, to everything familiar to him, to his entire world? How can a twelve-year-old boy separate forever from his beloved grandma Rosa and his Unchi Adrian? Will they ever meet again?"

"What's wrong with staying here?" Her lip trembled. "We have everything we need. A house, clothes, and food to put on the table. We survived those dreadful Nazis. Now you want us to go?"

"But Aurica, my beloved wife, wouldn't you like to be free? Never to worry about your rights ever again. Aren't you tired of living in fear?" He paused for a minute and added, "Don't you want a better future for Yossi?"

She lowered her eyes, and, after a moment, nodded.

"Children adjust quickly." He wrapped his arms around her. "We will too. You'll see, we'll have a wonderful life."

The truth was that Aurel's biggest fear was the communist regime in Romania, which was backed up by the Securitate. After the regime change, new laws started popping up like mushrooms in the underbrush. Under the new Communist Party, people would often vanish without a trace. Aurel figured they were being tortured or executed, if they dared to criticize the communist regime. Phone lines were installed with listening devices, letters were censored with thick black markers, and people were arrested for receiving a postcard with greetings from family in another country.

Civilians were paid to eavesdrop on their neighbors, old acquaintances, family members, or co-workers about half sentences or just single words that might be understood as a critique of the regime leaders. Informants would receive a nice bonus if they were able to convince mentally ill people to admit to being an enemy of the state, who were then often executed within twenty-four hours.

Aurel learned all about it from his mother-in-law Rosa. She begged him to take his family away. Rosa was the one who bribed the "right people" to get certificates for her family.

"Come with us," Aurel begged. "We are your family! We will take care of you."

"I'm old and blind." Rosa laughed. "No new country will want me. I'll stay here with Adrian. Don't worry, he will care for me. When the time comes, we will meet again."

Aurel knew Rosa's wishes, but never told Aurica. There was no reason to make her worry or upset. Once the certificates arrived and the travel documents were ready, he pleaded with Aurica to start packing.

"And what about my mother?" Tears welled up in her eyes. "How can I say goodbye to her? Who will take care of the woman who has cared for me all her life? Who will help her in the difficult moments?"

"Adrian promised to take care of her," Aurel answered with endless patience. "She will continue to live here at home with Adrian, and we will write them letters and visit whenever we can. I promise. Things will get better someday."

#

The Rosenthal family only had three days to pack their belongings. They were forbidden to take any Romanian currency or valuables. In a particularly humiliating ceremony, their Romanian papers were cut up in front of their eyes and thrown into their faces. The boy's medal from *Hashomer Hatzair*[23] that Yossi proudly wore on his shirt was ripped off and thrown into the trash.

In complete silence, the family was forced to say goodbye to their loved ones, before they hurried to the Constanța's port to board the *Transylvania*.

23 A Zionist, secular Jewish youth movement, founded in 1913 in Austria-Hungary.

"Goodbye," Aurica whispered to her mother, who held her and Yossi. They wept bitterly.

"Take care of yourself for me," Rosa whispered in a strangled voice.

Tears choked their throats as they looked back one last time at the only home they had ever known, and the family they were leaving behind.

"*La revedere*[24], Romania," whispered Aurel. He threw the silver key to their home into the blue water as the ship set off.

#

The sea voyage was unbearably difficult. The conditions on the ship were intolerable. The passengers were cramped among thousands of passengers, and the high ocean waves caused many to vomit into the navy-blue water.

Aurica huddled under the deck's stairs, next to the railing, close to another woman, whose complexion was greenish.

"I'm sorry," she said, when she noticed that her knee bumped into the other woman's leg.

"There is nothing to apologize for," said the other woman, smiling at her. Aurica's brown eyes met her companion's blue ones. "I'm Eva-Sophia," the other woman said, holding out her hand. "In Israel, they will call me Hannah."

"I'm Aurica." She shook the other woman's hand weakly. "In Israel, I will be called Golda." She smiled back.

"My husband must be hanging out there with our daughters," said Eva-Sophia, pointing to a distant point at the end of the ship.

"My husband and our son Yossi are probably playing a pirate game somewhere on board."

Both women smiled fondly.

---

24 Goodbye in Romanian.

"Well, speaking of imagination, do you know that my husband promised the girls they could pick oranges straight from the trees in Israel?" Eva-Sophia giggled.

"You win," said Aurica. "I don't think that even my husband could come up with something so fanciful." They laughed.

The two women spent the next few days getting to know each other better, sharing their biggest regrets, fears, and their hopes for a better future for their children.

#

It was late Wednesday, almost sunset, when a voice was suddenly heard. "There! Look over there. Land!"

Everybody stood up, laughing, cheering, and hugging.

Aurica and Eva-Sophia hugged each other. Aurel hugged Yossi and, with a trembling voice, whispered, "We're home."

When the ship docked on the coast of Haifa, the passengers were exhausted but excited to touch the land of their ancestors. Some people bent down and kissed the ground, others whispered a prayer.

A large sign in Hebrew greeted them. "Welcome to the *Sha'ar Ha-'aliyah*[25]!"

"Do you see that sign?" Aurel pointed. "It's in our language!"

After presenting their travel certificates, the passengers were disinfected, went through medical tests, and got vaccinated. Hours passed before they were finally issued an official immigrant certificate. They were given a light meal and beds in a shared tent, with white sheets on which was written, "The Jewish Agency."

Five days later, the Rosenthals were transferred to the Kfar Hasidim transit camp, close to the city of Haifa. They got a tent for their family.

---

25 Welcome to the Gate of immigration.

The conditions in the transit camp were harsh. The strong winds and the unrelenting rain caused floods that swept through the tents and soaked the immigrants to the bone. Field mice and other wildlife were regular guests in their home. Aurica wept bitterly, while squeezing the water from their few personal items. She begged her husband to change his mind, to let them return to Romania. Aurel refused. He asked her to be a little more patient, promised that these were only temporary conditions, and everything would work out soon.

On cold nights, when the thunder shook the earth and the lightning cut through the sky, Aurel would hug Yossi in his arms, wrap Aurica's head in a dry towel, and hum a tune he remembered from his childhood. His father used to sing it to him and his brother on cold stormy nights. It was a song in Yiddish about the end of war, soldiers coming home with hope in their hearts, knowing that everything would be better now. Aurel would think of his brother, wishing he too had returned home.

Aurel understood that his family's success depended on him adjusting quickly to his new identity as an Israeli. The sooner he felt he belonged, taking part in establishing the new developing country, the greater his chance of finding a job, learning the language, and integrating into the society.

Aurel worked days and nights to learn the Hebrew language. He enrolled Yossi in the Kol Israel Haverim – Alliance school. He knew the boy's curiosity and wisdom would help him easily adapt to the language and social life.

And he was right. Yossi flourished. In a short time, Yossi managed to make friends and excel in his academic studies. Aurel was happy and proud.

Soon enough, Aurel managed to find a job at a fabric store, located in the Hadar HaCarmel neighborhood in Haifa. By August 1953, within two years of their arrival in Israel, Aurel managed to save enough money to put a down payment on a small apartment at 15 Ha'shalom Street in Haifa.

Aurel's Zionist dream had been fully achieved. He had a stable job, a healthy family, and a happy child, who grew up like any other Israeli boy.

On August 10, 1953, an emergency telegram was received at the Rosenthals' residency in Haifa. The brief telegram said, "She's home! We found her. Friddie is home."

Aurel and Yossi at transit camp, 1951

CHAPTER EIGHTEEN

Eva-Sophia, 1951, The voyage on the *Transylvania*

As Eva-Sophia's sky-blue eyes watched the high ocean waves, she couldn't help but wonder how her parents had managed to make this journey at their age.

Baruch, Fanya, and most of their children immigrated to Israel on the same ship six years earlier in October 1945, leaving Bucharest suddenly on a hot summer night.

Baruch was born in Lespezi, a small town located on a mountain peak in Western Moldova, Romania. His father, Rabbi Avraham Abramovici, was the only Rabbi in their hometown. He wished for his eldest son to become the next Jewish leader, upon his retirement. Baruch was miraculously blessed, not only with all the necessary skills and qualities reserved for rabbis, but also a beautiful, cantorial voice, as well as a love for music and singing. During the High Holidays, he was asked to assist and lead the congregation in songs and prayers, in front of his father's adoring eyes.

When the boy reached Bar-Mitzvah age, his soul was bound with the soul of his distant cousin, also a music lover, named Fanya.

Fanya and her family lived in the capital city, Bucharest. When Baruch turned eighteen years old, he decided to rebel. Despite his parents' wish for him to stay and become the next Rabbi of Lespezi, he packed up his belongings and traveled to Bucharest to marry Fanya. His father never forgave him for disobeying the plans he had for his son and refused to talk to him ever again.

In a short time, the young talented man became popular among the Jewish community in Bucharest. Thanks to his singing talents, he was offered a cantor position in Templul Coral. Eventually, he became a rabbi there.

Baruch and Fanya had five children, four girls and one boy. Eva-Sophia was their eldest daughter. For almost three decades, Baruch served the synagogue faithfully and advocated for modern Judaism that incorporated organ playing and choir singing into the prayers.

Meanwhile, the Legionary Movement, also known as the Iron Guard, was a political, extremist, and anti-Semitic movement that gained popularity in Romania as early as 1927. Corneliu Codreanu, the party's founder, was known for his hatred of foreigners, Jews, and communists. He supported terrorist acts against his enemies and drew inspiration from the Nazi party in Germany. Members of the movement called on Romanian farmers and ordinary citizens to join them, promising that, if they succeeded in seizing power, they would immediately expel all Jews from Romania, confiscate all Jewish property, and divide it among the poor Romanian people. In 1937, the number of supporters of the party reached one million. In a solemn and extravagant ceremony, the main party branch was opened at 40 Calea Victoria, Bucharest. The walls of the office were decorated with pictures of King Carol II, Mussolini, and Hitler.

The acts of massacre, murder, and terrorism committed by the soldiers of the Legionnaire movement were visible to all. They were carried out in broad daylight and in crowded places. The Legionnaires ordered that anyone who did not hold Romanian or German ID cards would be shot or thrown from the train carriages. Jewish-owned businesses were smashed. The Legionnaires took every opportunity to rape Jewish women and girls. The Romanian police were helpless, unresponsive, and sympathetic to the Legionary Movement. They would forgive the criminals easily.

When the Legionnaires knocked on the door of Baruch and Fanya's house, one afternoon in late March 1940, Eva-Sophia stood in the living room, holding her oldest daughter in her arms. The house was bustling, as Passover was just a few days away. The whole family was busy preparing the house. Eva-Sophia had just finished giving her daughter a bath. She wrapped her in a large white towel, while whistling a festive tune. A wonderful cooking smell came from the kitchen and filled the house.

The baby smiled and put her little arms up to hug her mom's neck. "And now, let's go get dressed." Eva-Sophia kissed her little nose, while the baby giggled with pleasure.

Hard knocks on the door tore through the peaceful afternoon and threatened to dislodge the door from its hinges. Eva-Sophia froze in her place. She looked at the door, lips thin.

"Who's there?" Eva-Sophia's mother hurried out of the kitchen and wiped her hands on her apron. Both women watched the door, wide-eyed.

"Open the door!" a shout burst through the door. "Now! Or we'll break it down."

Eva-Sophia recovered first. She took a deep breath. "Try not to worry," she whispered, "everything will be fine." She handed the baby over to her mother. She believed that, no matter who the people on the other side of the door were, they would not dare hurt an older woman holding a baby.

"Good afternoon." She opened the door, wearing a fake smile. Four soldiers in Romanian uniforms stood there, their blank stares watching her.

"Hello," replied an officer, his hand resting on a gun.

"How can I help you?" She tried to keep her smile.

The soldier opened the door wide and pushed it aside. "We're looking for the rabbi," the chief officer said briskly.

"I see," said Eva-Sophia. "May I ask, what do you need my father for?"

The officer ignored her question. "Please tell him to come here. Or would you rather I ask my officers to look for him? I'm afraid they will not be as kind as I am, you see."

"There's no need." Baruch entered the room. "How can I help you, gentlemen?"

"Hello, Rabbi," said the senior officer. "Would you mind accompanying us to headquarters?"

"Can we resolve the matter here?" the rabbi asked. "We're all a little busy, preparing for the holiday."

"Passover..." The officer grinned and stroked his mustache. "Yes, I understand." His eyes spat fire. "Actually, I insist you accompany us to headquarters." He stroked the gun that was tucked into his pants belt.

Eva-Sophia and Fanya cried out, each holding one of Baruch's arms.

"No need." Baruch hurried to put on his coat. "Do not worry about me," he whispered to his wife and kissed her cheek. "I'll be back soon."

Rabbi Baruch did not return that night. Fanya prayed to God to give her strength. Three days later, Rabbi Baruch came home. His eyes were dull and his face pale. He spoke little and only repeated the sentence, "Everything is fine now. Thank God."

#

Less than a year later, on Tuesday, January 21, 1941, the Legionnaires' Revolt broke out, sparking the Bucharest riots. General

Ion Antonescu, who was appointed Romania's Prime Minister and *Conducător*[26] by King Carol II, formed a 'national-legionary government', together with his partner, Horia Sima. But, in January 1941, Antonescu sought to remove Sima and the Legionnaires from his government. Sima and the Legionnaires were angry and showed their rage by harming those who were unable to defend themselves, the Jews.

At the same time, the Legionnaires, led by Horia Sima, sought to seize state power, and eliminate General Ion Antonescu. The Legionnaires' leaders targeted Antonescu, while the Legionnaires' soldiers and supporters targeted the Jews of Bucharest. In mad waves of fury, they burned synagogues, looted Jewish homes and businesses, and killed many Jewish residents, throwing their bodies out into the streets.

It was a cold Tuesday morning. The sun struggled to rise between the shutters. In Baruch's synagogue, the crowd of worshippers had already begun to congest the prayer benches. They were wrapped in their heavy winter coats, rubbing their hands together to warm up.

Rabbi Baruch stood behind the *bimah*[27], preparing for the morning Shacharit prayer. He had just finished tying the *tefillin*[28] box between his eyes, holding the white *tallit*[29] in his other hand. In the meantime, he hummed a sacred melody to warm up his voice.

A burst of gunfire tore through the air. Screams erupted all throughout the prayer house.

Baruch turned and saw the uniformed Legionnaires' soldiers storming inside. Bursts of gunfire shot in all directions. He felt a

26 The ruler of Romania.

27 The raised platform in the synagogue from which the Torah is read and services are led.

28 A small black leather box containing scrolls of parchment inscribed with verses from the Torah.

29 A white prayer shawl.

bullet hit his right knee. He bent down and shuffled to the side of the stage, diving behind cover.

His heart was beating fast. He struggled not to faint. In the corner of his eye, he saw Mr. Chernow rushing to the stage, with his son in his arms. Gunfire sounded in his direction, and he pulled his son closer to his body. A moment later, a heavy sound echoed as the father's and son's bodies collapsed close to where Baruch was hiding. A red puddle of blood spread out from them, and they did not move.

Baruch, nursing his destroyed knee, watched a few people escape through the side door. But there was no way to reach it—he, like most of the other worshippers, was cut off by gunfire.

He knew he had to act fast to save his people. He prayed that his wife and children were safe, and then looked around. He saw the Stettgart children, hiding under the stairs. He waved at them, trying to send them a comforting smile. There were four of them. Amy, who was four years old, and three of her older brothers, all under the age of ten. They were immobilized. He saw the fear in their eyes. A sharp pain stabbed through his knee, but he decided to ignore it.

Baruch crawled towards the kids, panting. When he reached them, he picked up Amy in his arms and steered the kids quickly to the curved wooden stairs behind the *bimah* leading to his office. His heart was pounding. The shots never ceased.

He opened the walk-in book cabinet behind the closet door and hid the kids there. "Bend down, under the bookshelf, I must go help the others," he whispered. "Stay here. No one will hurt you."

"No, please," cried little Amy, refusing to let him go. She held his arms tightly. The boys didn't say a word, but Baruch could detect a strong smell of urine.

"Okay. I'll stay with you for a moment, but then I must go," he whispered. They all sat folded up, holding their knees in their hands. Amy was shaking. A lullaby song in Yiddish came to his mind, and he started singing it quietly. His mom used to sing it to him when he was very young, and he would sing it to his own children. It was about soldiers coming back home at the end of the war with hope in their hearts. As he sang, Amy didn't say a word. But her shaking stopped. When he was done, the children breathed softly.

In fact, there was no sound anywhere. He couldn't hear any more gunshots.

"I must go now," he whispered to the kids. "You must stay here. I'll come back to get you, as soon as I can."

He crawled out, his knee pulsating. Everything was quiet. He hoped that, once he opened the door of his office, he would only find friendly faces.

Baruch slowly began to climb the stairs towards the *bimah.* He didn't know that little Amy was following him.

When he got back upstairs, no one was there. The place was a disaster. He saw bodies scattered across the synagogue in pools of blood. The shooters were gone, but his congregation was also silent. The pain in his knee was by now unbearable. The room around him became dark. Baruch collapsed and lost consciousness.

When Baruch woke up, he found himself inside a military truck, among dozens of wounded or dead bodies. The pain in his leg was unbearable. He managed to breathe. The truck started to move.

"Hear, O Israel," his lips whispered as he looked out and saw the synagogue that he loved so much rising in flames. He thought of the children hiding in his office and screamed.

About 130 Jews were killed in the Bucharest riots, during the two days on which the Legionnaires' Revolt took place. Jewish neighborhoods were set aflame. The Legionnaires' headquarters became centers of torture, to which Jews were brought after being abducted from their homes. Jewish men were tortured and beaten. Women were raped in front of their husbands and children. They were thrown from the windows of the upper floors of the police headquarters.

A group of fifteen Jews, including a four-year-old girl, were taken to a slaughterhouse. They were cruelly murdered and hung on a meat hook. The little girl was Amy, Baruch realized, when he saw her body. The inscription "Kosher meat" was engraved on her corpse.

Two days later, Romanian Prime Minister Ion Antonescu sent the army troops to end the Legionnaires' uprising. Cannons and tanks of the Romanian army stormed the streets of Bucharest and, within a few hours, regained control. Eva-Sophia and the rest of her family were hidden in her parents' basement, and they did not emerge until Baruch returned home. They, like the Rosenthal family many streets away, waited out the riots. When Baruch returned, he was haunted. Meanwhile, the Legionnaires fled and sought refuge. Sima Horia found refuge in Germany, while Antonescu marched through the streets of Bucharest to reassert his power.

The march ended in front of the Prime Minister's House, where Romanian and German troops cheered for Antonescu. Antonescu took care to hide from the public the massacre carried out on the Jewish community in Bucharest.

A few months later, in June of that year, riots broke out against the Jews of Iași, killing thousands, including David and Sophie Postelnic and their four daughters; a family the Abramovici family did not know, but would be intertwined with, nonetheless.

It took a long time for the Jewish community in Bucharest to reestablish itself, if at all. The disaster of the massacre left its mark everywhere. People worked hard to rebuild the synagogues and find a safe haven again. Baruch's community bonded together to rebuild their synagogue. As he and his family reconstructed his office, Baruch insisted that a secret compartment be built behind his bookcase, even larger than before.

Baruch and Fanya could not return to the way they had been before the pogrom. The light in Baruch's eyes dulled, and often he wept bitterly. When he found little Amy's body in the slaughterhouse, and her brothers' burned bodies in his old office in the synagogue, he swore he would never sing again. He wanted the Stettgart children to be the last ones to hear his songs.

He lay in bed the night he returned from the hospital with a cast on his knee, Fanya's arms around him, as she breathed softly. Baruch could not sleep. Tears kept flowing as the images of the massacre raged through his mind. He promised God and himself that he would do whatever he could to protect children, even at the cost of his own life.

Baruch dedicated the rest of his life to rescuing orphans. He contacted a Jewish underground organization called *Bricha*[30]. It operated in Bucharest, and Baruch became one of their main contacts. He often left the house quickly and quietly in the middle of the night, wearing dark clothing. He was requested to hide children or transfer them to another safe location. The walk-in bookcase in his restored office became a temporary shelter.

He never told anyone about his actions, not even Fanya or his children. The secret police still somehow managed to track him down. Although there was no clear evidence of any illegal actions on his side, he was often arrested and taken in for interrogation. They didn't want him dead. They believed he would lead them to the greater underground. For them, he was just a small fish. He knew he was on borrowed time, but he was not afraid. God was by his side.

One morning, visitors came to the synagogue. Baruch was busy at that time, taking off the *talith* from his shoulders and unwrapping his left arm from the *tefillin.* The morning prayers were over by now and Baruch was the last person left in the Temple.

"Hello?" asked Baruch when he saw the big sanctuary door open, and a young couple entered the room quietly. Although they both wore regular clothes, they seemed to be foreigners.

30 Meaning escape in Hebrew.

Baruch left the *bimah* and walked down the stairs toward the couple, with a welcoming smile.

"Shalom," said the young man, "we're looking for Rabbi Abramovici?"

Baruch smiled. "You've found him. How may I help you?"

"My name is Rafi, and this is Ilana. We're from the Joint organization. Have you heard about us?"

"Yes, of course," Baruch nodded. The American Jewish Joint organization was active in Bucharest, as well as other cities in Romania. They assisted Jewish communities after the war with food donations, clothes, and other supplies. "I'm honored to meet you," he said as he shook their hands.

"We need your help," said Ilana immediately. She kept scanning the room.

"No one else is here," Baruch said calmly. "Let's go to my office, shall we?" he suggested.

They nodded and followed him.

Baruch led them down the curving wooden stairs, still behind the *bimah.* They reached a small office with no windows, a small desk, and a few single chairs. The office was crowded with prayer books and a coat rack stood lonely in the corner. Behind the coat rack was another door for a small walk-in book closet.

"So, how can I help you?" asked Baruch as soon as they sat down.

"We have a few children who need your help."

"A few?" Rabbi Baruch raised his eyebrows.

Ilana looked somewhat nervous and bit her nails.

Baruch paused. He felt some tension in the air; something about this situation seemed strange to him. He didn't say anything and waited to hear what the purpose of their visit was.

"Yes." Ilana glanced around.

The young couple paused and looked at each other. "We also know you're in trouble," said Rafi slowly, "and we want to help you and your family escape."

Rafi and Ilana's visit to the synagogue did not surprise Baruch. He was often asked to accompany one group of children or another. But this time, the request was different. This time he, his wife, and his family were asked to accompany a group of orphaned children on their journey to Israel, on the ship called the *Transylvania*, and to help them settle there.

By October 15, 1945, within twenty-four hours after Rafi's and Ilana's visit to the synagogue, the forged travel documents were ready. Baruch and the others were forbidden to reveal their plans to anyone. They had to disappear suddenly and immediately.

The Rabbi and his wife did not hesitate for a moment. It was God's plan for them.

And so, in the middle of the night, the Abramovici family disappeared from Bucharest. They left behind their apartment and all their belongings. Only Eva-Sophia, their eldest daughter, stayed behind. She was in her ninth month of pregnancy with her second child and knew she could not withstand this journey.

"We will come to you as soon as we can," Eva-Sophia promised her parents and siblings. "May your path be blessed. I will find you when I reach the holy land."

Now, six years later, Eva-Sophia stood aboard the *Transylvania* ship and hugged her daughters. "There, in the Land of Israel, we will be reunited with our family," she promised. "No more persecution, no more fear, no more bloodshed."

When she looked up, she saw Aurica's eyes smiling at her. Aurica hugged her son, Yossi, and whispered similar things in his ears.

CHAPTER NINETEEN

Friddie, 1953, Bucharest

The black car halted near Tanti Gisela's and Unchi Victor's house. Friddie got out of the car and knocked gently on the heavy door. She wondered what she would find there, behind the door. Her family had gone through the massacre and the war, the looting against the Jews, and the decrees of the communist regime.

Mircea waited patiently in the car. He offered to accompany her, but Friddie refused. "I must meet my family alone," she said. "I must confront my past and my fears by myself." He understood. He always understood her.

On the way to her Tanti Gisela's home, Mircea told Friddie the little information he managed to gather about her family. He realized from the few conversations they'd had in the labor camp behind the stone wall, how important family was to her.

Months before, when he was taken from the labor camp, he passed out in the car, due to the drugged hood they'd put on him. When he woke up, he found himself in a small, clean office. After a moment, the senior commander who had visited the labor camp walked in. He had recognized Mircea in the labor camp. When the commander had returned to headquarters, he ordered that Mircea be released immediately and brought to him.

The commander offered Mircea a senior position in the Communist Party on the spot. Mircea refused, politely but stubbornly. He thanked the commander for freeing him from the labor camp and begged him to do his best to assist in Friddie's release, as well. The officer, who remembered the generosity of Mircea's father, agreed.

There, the officer also gave him a stack of letters. Mircea's mother had written from Switzerland, though her mail had been intercepted. The commander left the room and Mircea began to read through the letters. His mother had managed to escape capture when King Mihai was banished and found refuge in Switzerland. Shortly after she arrived, she married one of the descendants of the Grimaldi royal family of Monaco. He wrote back to her, and her reply came quickly. She begged him to come to Switzerland. He refused, unable to leave while Friddie remained at the labor camp.

When he was released from the office, he returned to Bucharest and rented a modest room. He kept writing to his mother and officials, to try and get Friddie out.

Now, he watched Friddie walk up to the door of the house. She knocked, her scarred knuckles hitting the heavy door with a tap. After a moment, the heavy door creaked. "Who are you?" an older woman whispered. She wore a faded light-blue dress that had seen better days, and a stained apron that partially covered the dress. She dried her hands on her apron. White hair covered the woman's head completely and her face looked tired and wrinkled for her fifty-nine years of age.

"Tanti Gisela." Friddie fell into the woman's arms. "It's me, Fridda."

"Fridda? Friddie? Is that you? Is that really you?" The woman's eyes widened, and her mouth spread into a grin.

Friddie burst into tears. "Yes, Tanti. It's me. I'm free."

"My God," Gisela sobbed and hugged Friddie in her arms, which felt weak around Friddie's torso. "My child, my dear child..."

Another set of arms hugged them both. "Oh, dear girl," Victor whispered, tears streaming down his cheeks. "What did they do to you?" he asked as he surveyed Friddie's scarred face and skinny body.

He led the two women to the couch and supported them both as they sank into the pillows.

Friddie looked around. The walls of the apartment were empty of the rich pictures that had previously adorned the space. The statues had also disappeared, as well as the large chandelier that had hung from the ceiling and illuminated the room. The rugs that covered the floor were torn and worn out and the green curtains were faded beyond recognition. The empty space was dark and only a single ray of sunlight dared to penetrate the half-closed shutter. Friddie, in that moment, understood that the wars and pogroms had been hard on her family.

Friddie took a deep breath. "What about everyone? Mom? Dad? Tanti Rosa? I haven't seen my parents yet. I went to their house on Bulevardul Unirii and knocked on the door for a long time, but no one opened it. I thought maybe they had moved," she said, her throat choking.

"Oh, my poor girl," Gisela murmured. "You still don't know..."

"Don't know what?"

Victor hugged her shoulders. "You should be brave now, Fridda," he whispered. "We'll tell you everything, but you must be strong, okay?"

Friddie sobbed when she heard about the death of her father, and her mother's loss of sanity. Her tears continued when she learned of the death of Unchi David, his wife Sophie, and their young daughters, during the 1941 Iași pogroms. She cried as they told her of the fire that destroyed Tanti Zilli and Unchi Alexander's beautiful home in Constanța, the same house she had stayed in when she met Freddy. Then, after the fire, Unchi Alexander was forbidden to practice dentistry, because he was of Jewish descent. And no one knew about Tanti Feiga and her children's fate, since the last postcard she had sent, upon their arrival in Israel.

All these years, Friddie had tried to repress any memories of her beloved family. They were always accompanied by endless pain. Now, she was heartbroken by how her family had changed. She tried to remember how they were before, which made her feel overwhelmed with sorrow.

At least, she thought, Tanti Rosa is doing well, as are her children. Friddie was especially happy to hear that the Rosenthal family had found a new home in Israel.

"Oh, my dear Aurica, my beloved cousin," she smiled. "How is their little son Yossi doing?"

"He's not so little anymore," Victor replied. "The boy recently turned fourteen years old."

"One day, I will visit them in their new house in Israel," Friddie declared, wiping her eyes with her sleeve.

"Friddie." Gisela hesitated. "Tomorrow, when we go to visit your mother in the mental asylum... I want... I mean, it's important that you know something."

"What?" asked Friddie. "What else could possibly be wrong?"

"She's not so okay, your mother... I mean, in her head... She doesn't remember us; she doesn't know who we are. I don't want you to be disappointed, Friddie. She is very ill. After your father died, she lost hope of finding you. She was devastated. We sent her to the best hospital we could find. But she never came back to herself. Rosa and I visit her often, but she doesn't talk to us, nor to anyone else. She is mostly silent. If she doesn't remember you... you must understand... I don't want you to be disappointed."

Friddie looked down. "During all my teenage years, I didn't appreciate my parents. I did stupid things, I know. I only cared about my popularity and being rich. I wanted attention and gifts. I didn't appreciate what I had. I even dreamt of running away," Friddie laughed bitterly. "I knew my parents heard all the rumors. I knew the teachers complained to Dad and that he was summoned to the principal's office often. I just didn't care. I wanted to rebel, to break boundaries. I wanted to be free." She looked down at her hands, tears dripping off her cheeks onto her lap. "A free Romanian woman. But I was nothing but a spoiled girl. I smoked, I drank, I spent time with bad people, I did what I wanted, and they suffered because of me. I broke their hearts when I canceled my engagement to Nelu. And then, the wedding with Freddy. They warned me, but I did not listen." Her eyes filled with tears, and she sobbed, throwing her face in her hands. Her cries broke their hearts.

"I am so sorry," Friddie cried. "I just wish I could apologize to them. I wish they could forgive me."

Gisela hugged her shoulders. "Just take care of yourself now, Friddie," Gisela whispered. "That's the only thing you can do. That's what they would want for you, to be happy again. Do it, for their sake."

#

The streets of Bucharest were crowded and the sky was cloudy, as Friddie and her two aunts walked down the avenue to the mental asylum, where Elvira was hospitalized. On their way, they passed by the old post office building on Calea Victoriei, where Friddie was once arrested. It was an abandoned building now, with a neglected courtyard and shattered windows. A hiding place for homeless people. Friddie glanced at the building once, tightening her grip at her aunts' elbows.

The institution on Berceni Street was established in the early 1940s by Dr. Dishku, who originally immigrated from Germany.

Unlike other Romanian physicians, he did not see any risk to the greater society by slowly integrating his mentally disabled patients back into regular social life.

With the generosity of some of his friends, Dr. Dishku established a modest private institution, based out of a large house with two floors, surrounded by a high fence, in order to give his patients privacy. In front was a brass gate with a guard on duty. It usually remained open for visitors. The rooms of this institution were painted in happy colors and patients were allowed to walk in the gardens surrounding the house, whenever they felt comfortable to do so. This institution housed no more than thirty lucky patients.

Gisela hurried to the front door and signaled to a guard who knew her. "And who is this lovely lady?" the guard asked, gesturing to Friddie.

"She is my niece," Rosa hurried to reply, "Elvira's daughter."

"Aww... wow!" His mouth gaped open.

The smell of detergents greeted them as they opened the main door. The corridor on the first floor was partially empty and a few nurses hurried across the hallway. Rosa and Gisela led Friddie up the stairs to the second floor. They entered a large, noisy living room. The walls of the living room were painted in shades of greenish-pink and a painting of a large rainbow covered the central wall. A couple of chairs and sofas were spread around the room. A bookcase of shelves containing books and puzzle games leaned against another wall. A large radio was set in the corner of the room and played music. Most of the patients spent their time here. Nurses were walking about the room, or sitting next to patients, playing puzzles with them, and guiding them in reading books or newspapers.

Gisela held Friddie's elbow gently and pointed her to a lower desk at the back of the room. Friddie saw four women and a man sitting together, all wearing long green shirts and black pants. They were all staring at a large book, containing mostly art paintings, their mouths agape. They seemed to be having some sort of conversation, although Friddie couldn't understand any of their discussion. It sounded like a random mix of syllables and sounds.

Near to that table, in a faded green armchair, sat another woman. Her hair was white and shaggy, her body was slender and skinny, and the green shirt she wore hung off her skeletal frame. The woman stared blankly into space and said nothing.

"Mom, Mom." Friddie hurried towards her. Tears choked her throat. How was this possible? This woman was not at all the beautiful, tall, well-maintained woman who raised her. But those big, beautiful green eyes—Friddie could never mistake them. They were once so warm, so understanding, filled with endless love. But now, those eyes were empty. Hollow.

"Mom, look at me," begged Friddie and fell at her mother's feet.

Elvira looked down for a moment. Then, she stared again into the empty space.

"Mom, please, it's me. Your daughter, Friddie." Tears pooled in Friddie's own green eyes.

"I love you so much, Mommy. I missed you so much. I miss Daddy. I miss our family. All these years... Thirteen years away in prison, then in the labor camp... I cried so much, I agonized. My only hope was to see you, to hug you, to be back in your arms... Mom, please!"

Friddie held her mother's skinny hands and kissed them repeatedly. She begged to be hugged again, to feel safe. She longed to be her little girl again, even just for a short while.

Elvira was silent, staring blankly into space.

"Friddie..." Rosa put her hands on Friddie's shoulders. "She doesn't remember you. It's not your fault. She doesn't know what's happening around her. It's not her fault, either. I'm sorry, my dear child. She has been through a lot."

"Come on, Friddie, let's go," whispered Gisela and helped Friddie back to her feet. "We'll be back tomorrow. Maybe tomorrow will be a better day."

Rosa wiped the tears away from Friddie's face. "Oh, Friedda'lle," Rosa sighed. "It hurts so much, I know. We, Gisela and I, have tried so many times. We've been coming here for years now. Bringing her things, pictures, personal items. We thought—we hoped—that she would remember. Nothing. Not even a word. It's like her mind is shut off. I'm so sorry."

Friddie wiped her tears and took a deep breath "Okay, maybe tomorrow. We'll be back tomorrow and every day, until..."

"Goodbye, Elvira." Rosa bent down and kissed her sister's cheeks. Gisela did the same.

"Goodbye, Mom." Friddie kissed her mom's cheeks and hugged her. "I'll be back tomorrow. I promise."

#

For the next eight months, Friddie came back to visit her mom. She never missed a day. She would read articles from the newspaper and stories to her mother, the ones she thought she might like. She would tell stories about the men who visited the little hat store below where they used to live, like she did when she was a little girl. Friddie would weave their memories together into fantastic stories. Her mother, father, and Friddie would all be major characters, and she would bring in family pictures, to go along with the tales. Once, she brought in her mom's wedding ring. Sometimes, rarely, her mother would even smile.

One day, Dr. Dishku took Friddie aside and explained the situation to her. "Your mom went through intensive traumatic and stressful events that damaged her brain function. It affected her physical ability to function, as well as her ability to control her emotions, memory, and reasoning. You must understand, Friddie.

She has impaired brain function. Mrs. Stoleru will never regain her cognitive skills, meaning she will never be able to speak, nor recognize any of her acquaintances or family members."

"You don't know my mom," said Friddie confidently.

"You're a good girl, Friddie," said the doctor, "and we all appreciate what you're doing for your mom, but I just don't want you to be heartbroken. I'm afraid the diagnosis is not in our favor this time, my child," he said, patting her on the shoulder.

Friddie refused to give up. She was confident that her mom was there, that somewhere deep inside, she was aware of her surroundings but couldn't find the words to communicate back. They just needed to be patient and give her more time. She would never lose hope. She owed it to her mom, to her family. But with each passing day, Friddie got a little weaker. Her mood was gloomy and, at the end of each day, when she returned to the small apartment she now shared with Mircea, she collapsed on the bed, soaking their bed with her tears.

Mircea was there for her. He supported and encouraged her not to lose hope. Every night, he would pick up the pieces and look deep into Friddie's green eyes. "You're doing the right thing," he assured her. "There's always hope."

Mircea now operated on several fronts. He got a job as an engineer within a government office. At the same time, he exchanged letters with his mother, and they planned his and Friddie's escape from Romania. Mircea's mom was trying to use her marriage into the Grimaldi royal family to get them the required paperwork.

Mircea, who refused to comply with the communist regime in Romania, knew that as ex-political prisoners, both he and Friddie were under surveillance. They would never be safe in Bucharest. As a collaborator with the previous royal palace, and hence a "potential threat" to the existing regime, he would never find peace in their homeland. Friddie was in no less danger, but she refused to leave, because of her mother. Mircea was patient, though worried about their status.

One evening, when Friddie came back home exhausted and sad from her visit to the mental asylum, Mircea asked to talk with her. After they finished eating dinner and cleaned the dishes, he asked Friddie to sit on the couch in their living room for a moment. Friddie was tired. She sank into the blue armchair and closed her eyes.

Mircea knelt before her. He took a ring out of his pocket. It was a simple golden ring with a small red diamond. He handed Friddie the ring and said, "Dear Friddie, I'm sorry I can't afford to buy you a bigger ring, as you deserve. You are the joy in my life. The reason I wake up in the morning and can still enjoy the sunlight. Please, my dear, please make me the luckiest man in the universe and say yes."

Friddie smiled. She held the ring close to her heart.

"My Mircea," she whispered, and tears welled up in her eyes. "I don't need money and wealth. I don't need expensive shoes and extravagant dresses and perfumes. I don't need to travel the world. I just want to be happy, healthy, and alive. With you. I'll be honored to be your wife."

Friddie and Mircea's wedding ceremony took place in City Hall on October 20, 1954. It was also Friddie's thirty-fifth birthday. They held a modest and formal service. Friddie wore a long green dress and black high heels she borrowed from Rosa, which were a size too big. Gisela lent her a green lace hat that matched her dress. Mircea wore a brown suit and polished leather shoes he borrowed from a friend.

As the official asked Mircea to place the ring on Friddie's finger, he gave her a soft smile. He slipped the silver ring with the small purple gem in the center on her finger and whispered, "I love you, my wife." Friddie stared down at the silver ring in awe. Rosa must have given him her ring; the ring she had managed to save all those years, the ring Rosa's Tata gave her Mama as a symbol to their eternal love. Friddie hiccupped with sobs, clutching the family heirloom to her chest.

Gisela and Rosa hurried to hug and kiss the couple. Victor shook Mircea's hand affectionately.

Once the ceremony was over, Friddie rushed to the mental asylum to share the news with her mother.

"Mom, look," Friddie said excitedly as she entered the room. Elvira was lying in bed and gazing at the empty space. The nurse worked alongside Elvira's bed, arranging the pillows and brushing Elvira's long, white hair.

"I got married today," Friddie said, kissing her mom on the forehead. "And also, it's my birthday. The day you gave birth to me. Remember?"

A spark ignited in Elvira's green eyes. It seemed as if she was looking at Friddie's hands, looking for the wedding ring.

"Here, Mom." Friddie took off the ring and placed it in her mom's hands. "It was your mother's. Do you remember?"

Elvira looked at the ring, fingering the simple jewelry. She said nothing.

"Congratulations, Friddie," said the nurse with a smile. "I'm sure your mom is very happy for you."

Friddie thanked her, with a smile.

"I know you'd like him, Mom. He's a kind and loving man, just like you and Dad always wanted me to marry," Friddie said. "He's tall and handsome, and he lives simply. We will have a good life together, Mom. You can come live with us. The apartment is modest, but we are happy."

Elvira didn't say a word and just gazed blankly at the ring. Her face was frozen, and her eyes were hollow. There was no sign that she understood anything Friddie said.

"So." Friddie's eyes filled up with tears. She quickly suppressed them. "What would you like to do today, Mom?" She tried to sound happy. "How about we put some makeup on you? You'll look so pretty and elegant." Suddenly, Friddie remembered how she loved to watch her mother getting ready to leave the house, putting on makeup, brushing her hair, trying on an infinite number of dresses and hats. Friddie felt a sharp pinch in her heart.

Friddie picked up her bag and started digging through, looking for her mascara and blush. She pulled out some eye shadows, lipstick, and nail polish.

"I'll leave you two alone now," said the nurse and left the room.

"You're going to look so pretty, Mom." Friddie touched the brush lightly in the blush.

#

It was late afternoon when Friddie finally left the asylum. She opened the gate, waving goodbye to the guard on duty. By now, she knew all the staff at the asylum; the nurses, the doctors, the admin, and the supporting staff. She became friends with them, appreciating how they cared for her mom. She took the time to get to know each one of them, inquired about their well-being and their families. Often, she would bring in a cake to celebrate a staff member's birthday, retirement, or another happy occasion.

The sky was dark and the weather was cold as she started walking back to the apartment. She hugged her coat closer to her body to keep herself warm. A few minutes later, she remembered that she had forgotten to pack up her makeup and put it back in her purse. She turned around and started walking back.

"Forgot something?" the guard asked. Friddie nodded and climbed up the stairs to her mother's room. She found the makeup set exactly where she had left it, on the table next to her mom's bed. Friddie stood there for a minute, watching her mom sleeping peacefully. Her eyes were closed, and she was breathing quietly. She kissed her mom on the forehead again gently, so as not to wake her up. When Friddie bent down to pick up her makeup from the lower shelf of the side table, she could swear that she felt her mother's hand touching her head gently, petting her. A chill went through her bones.

"Mom?" She looked up.

"Yes?" Elvira whispered, her eyes still closed.

"Mom," Friddie exclaimed. She could swear that she felt her mom's energy back in the room.

Elvira didn't open her eyes, but kept her hand on Friddie's head.

"Mom, can you hear me?" Tears choked Friddie's throat.

Elvira didn't say a word. Her eyes remained closed, but her face filled with light.

"Nurse! Doctor!" Friddie screamed in excitement. "Come here, come here quickly!"

A couple of nurses and doctors rushed into the room.

"You know," Elvira's voice sounded clearly in the room, "I used to have a daughter, as pretty as an angel." Her face beamed. She took a breath and continued, "But now, I have nothing. No daughter, no husband, just nothing." Her face darkened at once.

"No, Mom, no!" Friddie cried, "I'm right here, Mom. Look at me! I'm your daughter, Friddie. I'm back with you. Look at me, Mom, please."

Elvira opened her eyes. She looked straight into Friddie's eyes and then scanned the room. She looked at the doctors and nurses surrounding her bed. A light reignited in her eyes but quickly faded. She closed her eyes again and, for the very last time, in front of Friddie, the nurses, and doctors, she took her last breath.

#

Elvira's funeral took place the next morning. It was raining, and the family huddled under black umbrellas by the fresh grave and wept. Friddie laid flowers on the dirt that covered her mother's grave and sobbed into a handkerchief that Mircea handed her.

"I am an orphan now," she cried. "Other than you, I have no one to care for me as my parents did."

A month later, Friddie and Mircea boarded the train that took them to Switzerland. Mircea's mother had sent him fake papers months earlier, but he did not tell Friddie until a week after her mother died. Now that they had nothing keeping them in Bucharest, the couple decided to leave. Mircea feared that the Romanian authorities would stop them. But the couple had their fake passports, and Mircea's mother had also paid the border patrols a huge sum of money to overlook the newlywed couple on their way to their honeymoon. They managed to cross Romania's borders with no difficulty.

Mircea breathed a sigh of relief as the train wheels touched Swiss soil. Friddie looked out the train window at this new city and wondered when she would see her family again. She knew it would be a long time. She prayed that, one day, she and Mircea could return to Romania, that one day, life would return to normal.

Friddie and Mircea rented a modest apartment on the shores of Lake Geneva. They lived a simple life and formed a circle of loving and supportive friends. Mircea found a job at the National Library of Geneva. He enjoyed his quiet work. Friddie discovered a love and talent for embroidery. Soon, their home was filled with pillows and blankets, embroidered in bright and happy colors.

Despite their many attempts, Friddie was unable to conceive. The trauma her body had endured during the thirteen years she had been imprisoned had destroyed any chance of her having a child. They mourned their loss.

A stray cat that passed by their home was invited to stay. She soon gave birth to six kittens that were all adopted by the couple. Occasionally, as the cats snuggled on their knees, Friddie and Mircea felt like they had the family they had always needed.

After all, it was a cat that led to their meeting behind the stone wall, who gave them hope in a place where there was none.

Friddie and Mircea, Geneva, 1959

Friddie and Mircea, Geneva, 1963

Friddie and Mircea, Geneva, 1965

Friddie is learning to drive! 1967

Friddie and Mircea, Geneva, July 1975

Friddie and a friend, Lake Geneva, Unknown year

CHAPTER TWENTY

Friddie and Mircea, 1961, Montreal, Canada

Only one thing marred Friddie's happiness. Even now, when she had finally found her new home, her safe place, there was one thing—one person—that came back and haunted her.

One evening, when Mircea returned home from the library, Friddie could no longer hide it. Her lips trembled as she took Mircea's hands.

"What happened, darling?" Mircea said, holding her.

"Mircea," Friddie whispered. "You have made me so happy. Your kind heart and your endless generosity fill my days. There's only one thing that keeps me awake at night. It gives me no rest."

"Tell me, dear. Tell me how I can help you."

"These pictures... The black-and-white photos they showed me in the interrogation room. The pictures of Freddy walking down the street next to a beautiful lady, the little girl, the boy on his shoulders... Are they real?"

He grimaced. "How can I know?"

"I need to ask you a favor," she whispered. "Now that we have some money, can we hire a private detective?"

Mircea let go of her and turned away. He rubbed his temples for a moment. "Why?" he asked. "Why now? Why is it so important to you?"

"No, darling!" Friddie held him from behind. "No, I'm not interested in him at all. It's just for me, for me to know. So that I can finally gain some closure about my past."

The next day, they met Mr. Oliver Müller in his office. Not only did they receive an excellent recommendation about him, but he was from the United Kingdom, which gave him more resources to work with. Friddie knew only a few minor biographical details about her ex-husband, Mr. Frederick Karl. She had no pictures of Freddy, either. All her personal belongings remained in the apartment when she left that morning, so many years ago, to meet him at the post office. The apartment to which she had never returned.

"It's a difficult task what you ask of me." Mr. Müller rubbed his eyes. "Without pictures, or other means of identification, it is almost impossible."

"Please. Please do your best," Friddie begged.

Mr. Müller ran a hand over his beard. "If I may ask you, why? Why do you desire to meet this man?"

"Because of this person, I went through hell. I think, at least, I deserve an explanation," she said.

The detective nodded. "I will try my best."

To the surprise of Friddie and Mircea, about a week later, Mr. Müller asked the couple to return to his office.

As they sat down next to the wooden desk, Mr. Müller turned his attention to two thick photo albums, laid out on the table. "Take a good look at the pictures in front of you. If there's anything you recognize, anything that draws your attention, it can be just a hunch or a gut feeling, please let me know right away. It's especially important that you observe each person's eyes. Details like hair, beard or mustache can be replaced or removed easily. Hair colors can be changed. The facial skin, wrinkles and facial expressions can change over time. The eyes will remain as they were before."

With a trembling hand, Friddie opened the cover of the first photo album and began looking at the photos. Her heart pounded hard. She curled her fingers into Mircea's hand.

"Take your time, Friddie," Mircea said. "I'm right here with you."

"Each album has close to 400 photos," Detective Müller said. "Most of them are brown, gray, black-and-white colors, but some were taken in faded colors, as well. As you will notice, the albums have images of both men and women. Since you mentioned you had seen a woman who may be related to Mr. Karl, I thought to include pictures of women in the albums, as well. Take your time, Mrs. Choiboteru, and take a good look."

"Who are the people in these pictures?" Mircea asked.

"Well, since Mrs. Choiboteru mentioned that, during her interrogations, she was asked questions about Mr. Karl being a foreign agent, I thought we should start there. There's a group of people who used to be part of one spy or espionage network, people who acted in "hostile" countries or in the countries behind the Iron Curtain." He took a deep breath and continued. "Some of the people here are no longer with us. Some have mysteriously disappeared, or their trace was lost. And there are some here, I believe, that we can still trace. I hope your Mr. Karl is in the third category."

It didn't take long for Friddie to find something. A couple of minutes later, she exclaimed, "Here, it's him. I'm sure!"

"Very good," said Mr. Müller and pulled out the picture of the man Friddie identified. He turned the picture over. "Frederick Karl, you said. According to this, his real name is John Antoine Alexander II."

A week later, Friddie and Mircea showed up at Detective Müller's office for the third meeting. The report was ready.

"John Antoine Alexander II, divorced with two children. He was born in France to a diamond dealer father and a mother who was born in Romania. She fled with her family before World War I and found refuge in Toulouse, southwestern France. At the age of seven, John Antoine immigrated with his family to Montreal, Canada, where later he married his high school sweetheart. They gave birth to a son and a daughter. At the age of twenty-seven, he got involved in an arms and drug deal. The primary dealer escaped, leaving John and his friends with huge debts. It was then that British Intelligence intervened and took advantage of John Antoine's knowledge of French and his family's Romanian background. They trained John and sent him to gather intelligence in Belgium, Switzerland, and Romania."

Detective Müller paused. Mircea pulled a handkerchief out of his pocket and wiped Friddie's eyes.

"Shall I continue?" Mr. Müller asked.

"Yes, please," Mircea replied. "It's important for us to hear everything."

"In 1940, John Antoine fled back to Canada, when he realized he was in great danger on one of his travels through Eastern Europe. There, he hid in Montreal, where his wife became the main breadwinner of the household. He became an alcoholic. The intelligence network compensated him by sending him several envelopes with cash to his address in Bucharest, but he never received them and complained loudly. They eventually shunned him when they realized he was no longer in Europe, and therefore no longer useful. These envelopes, with the unmarked banknotes, aroused the suspicion of the Romanian authorities and led them to attach a tiny listening device inside his apartment in Bucharest. They hoped that the contact person, meaning you, Friddie, would lead them to Freddy. But he was already gone. A year after he returned to Montreal and became a lazy alcoholic, his wife left him and took their two children away. Over the years, he has mostly lived on unemployment benefits."

"Anything else?" Mircea asked.

"Unfortunately, no. That's all the information I was able to gather."

"Thank you very much," said Mircea, shaking Mr. Müller's hand. "Now we come to closure." He squeezed Friddie's shoulders as he walked her to the door.

"One more thing," Mr. Müller suddenly said. "I don't know if it interests you, but take it." He handed Mircea a folded piece of paper.

"What is it?" Mircea asked.

"His address," the detective said. "If you happen to be in Montreal and want to pay a visit."

#

The wheels of the plane screeched against the ground. It turned and heaved as it parked on the tarmac next to the terminal. "Ladies and gentlemen, welcome to Montreal International airport," came the captain's voice. Friddie tightened her coat. Although she was accustomed to wintry, snowy weather in Romania, it was a particularly frigid winter in Canada.

After checking their passports and collecting their luggage, Friddie and Mircea hurried to catch a taxi that took them to their hotel. They planned to stay there no more than three nights, confront the past, and return to their warm nest in Geneva.

Friddie had hardly said a word since boarding the plane in Geneva. She barely managed to sleep in the weeks leading up to this trip. When she did, her tossing and turning from nightmares woke Mircea. He got out of bed before sunrise, yawning and stretching his aching back. He went to the window, leaning against the old frame. The hotel they chose was located in the center of Montreal. From their room, Mircea could see lights sparkle against the mountain nearby.

"It's beautiful here," Mircea said at breakfast that morning. "Very unique."

"I just want to get it over with," Friddie said, barely touching her coffee. "To put it behind me."

"Of course." He squeezed her hand.

The taxi arrived. Mircea gave the driver the address.

Less than twenty minutes later, the taxi halted near a low and neglected house. Mircea paid the driver and stepped out of the car. He reached out a hand to Friddie. "Come, my dear," he said, trying to smile reassuringly.

Friddie held Mircea's arm and looked at the house in front of them. It was run-down, made of bricks that looked like they wanted to jump out of the wall. A large yard made up the front of the house, but it seemed that no one had bothered to nurture or cut the grass in years. The tiled roof was broken, and the first step was missing as well. Friddie and Mircea had to skip over it, so as not to fall.

"Ready?" Mircea plastered on an encouraging smile.

Friddie nodded, even though she was not.

Mircea rang the bell.

No sound was heard. Mircea waited another moment and knocked on the door.

"Yeah, yeah, damn it. I heard you," a voice behind the door said. Heavy footsteps followed.

The door creaked open, and eyes peered through a narrow crack.

"Who the hell are you and what do you want?"

Friddie was silent. Her face was pale. She felt like she was in shock. "We're looking for Mr. John Antoine Alexander II," said Mircea.

"You found him. Now, who the hell are you?"

Friddie came back to life. Her face grew red. She pushed open the door and stormed into the room. "Are you still asking who we are? How dare you?" Her eyes spat fire and rage. It seemed that all the anger that had been stored in her was about to erupt.

"Look at me!" she shouted. "Remember me? You monster!"

"Friddie..." Mircea said and hurried in after her.

In the dim light, they saw an old man, slightly bent over, in his sixties, neglected. His face was red, and the bristles of his beard suggested that he had not showered or shaved for several days. He wore a plaid robe over a sweatshirt, and a stench of alcohol swelled around him. Friddie looked the room over. Rotting food and beer cans were scattered across the floor. Even on the lone couch, she could spot crumbs decorating the rough fabric.

The man looked at Friddie's face in astonishment. He was confused. It took him another long moment and suddenly there was a glow in his eye.

"Friddie," he said. "Is that you?"

"But of course, who else? Your wife, remember? The one you married. The woman you swore to love and honor, to be faithful to. The one you made a child with and then ran away like a dog with fleas. Now, do you remember?"

"Oh, Friddie... You have changed." His voice sounded surprised and disappointed at the same time.

"I've changed? You're a piece of dirt. Look at yourself! Look in the mirror and see nothing more than dirt. Sit down!" she commanded him.

"What?"

"I said, sit down!" She pushed him towards the couch. "Let's see if we can refresh your memory." Her voice was furious.

"Friddie, listen, I'm sorry..."

"No, no, it's too late now. I don't want your pathetic sorrow. I don't want your excuses. You, you had another wife, you had children.

They threw me in jail because of you. They raped and tortured me. You allowed it to happen. I was innocent. I believed in you. I was waiting for you to save me. You? You had enough time to save me, if you wanted to. Have you ever thought about me? Did I ever cross your mind? Me? Your wife? The mother of your child? Where is my child, do you know?" Tears choked her throat.

"Friddie… Right... We had a child. I remember that now. You were pregnant..."

"God has graced me with freedom from you and saved the child from growing up in the shadow of a father like you. How much I loved you at first. How much I hated you after."

"Friddie, I want to apologize," he said.

"Do you think I can ever forgive you? Do you think that one word can erase the thirteen years I spent in prison? In the death camps? Being tortured? I lost my family because of you. My sanity. The children I can never give birth to. Oh no. I will never forgive you. I will never let you clear your conscience in one word. I will never forgive you, you hear? Never! But do you know what…" She paused for a minute, "I do forgive myself."

The room became silent for a long time.

"Friddie..." Mircea said finally. "I think it's time to go home."

"Just one more thing." Friddie turned to John Antoine again. "Tell me, just one thing. Why? What was I for you? Why did you make me fall in love with you and then leave me in pain? Why?"

"Why..." John Antoine murmured. "They told me I had to find someone, a cover story, otherwise people would suspect me, a handsome man but single. Who would believe me? Who would deliver information to an unmarried man with no family? I could never become one of them. They sent me cash, a lot of money in mixed currencies, in big envelopes. I had to pick it up from mailbox #67 with instructions. Do you understand? You, Friddie… you were just a cover story, nothing else. Just a cover."

CHAPTER TWENTY ONE

Friddie and Golda: The Letters

Haifa, Israel, January 1959

My dear cousin Friddie,

I sent you a letter last month but didn't get any response. I hope your address has not changed.

I miss you, my dear cousin and friend. I miss our families; I miss our life in Romania. I miss our Tante, I miss our culture, even just walking down our familiar streets.

Israel is good to me. The people are kind, but there is nothing like being at home. I've been here for eight years so far and I'm still slowly learning the Hebrew language. Aharon, in his endless patience, teaches me, word by word. Yossi also helps. The weather here and the humidity are harsh, but as you know, we will get used to it in the end.

Take care of yourself, my beloved. Kiss Mircea for me.

Missing you,
Aurica (in Israel, I'm called Golda)

***

Geneva, Switzerland, March 1959

Golda, my beloved cousin,

I was so happy to receive your letter. I am happy to hear that you're all doing well, and that Israel is kind to you. I sincerely hope that one day we can meet again.

Before we left for Geneva, I spent some time with my beloved Tanti Rosa. I am sad that her eyesight is deteriorating, but I'm glad that your brother Adrian was able to convince her to visit the mountains she likes so much. I hope the mountain air does her some good.

How is your husband, Aharon, and your dear son, Yossi? I imagine he has grown so much by now. I am so proud of you that you have fulfilled your dream. Dreams are meant to come true, even if the process is sometimes difficult.

Take care of yourself. Kiss everyone for me.

Yours,
Friddie

***

Haifa, Israel, January 1961

Dear Friddie,

My heart is broken. The news of our Aunt Gisela's death struck me. So young and so beautiful. Is it possible?

My dear Friddie, is this how our family is doomed to suffer from illness and torment?

Hugging and crying,

***

Lyon, France, May 1964

My beloved Golda,

Thank you for the pictures you sent me. Without a doubt, you have a beautiful family. I can hardly believe that little Yossi has already turned

25 years old. So young and so handsome. I was happy to hear about his academic successes and the completion of his undergraduate degree. Honors in economics! So smart. Even when he was a toddler, he was so curious. I knew he would succeed and rise to greatness.

I am writing to you from the lovely city of Lyon. Mircea's mother passed away recently, and we took a couple days off to attend her funeral. My Mircea surprised me and bought us plane tickets. Lyon is so charming, the blend of the new and old makes it such a fascinating city.

Kissing you all,
Friddie

***

Haifa, Israel, February 1966

Friddie, my beloved cousin,

Thank you for your recent photos and postcards. It's great to see you and Mircea traveling the world and having fun. I especially liked your photos from the safari in Africa. Weren't you afraid to drive in an open jeep, surrounded by wild animals? I know how much you miss visiting our home town. I do hope that one day Romania will be willing to welcome us as tourists once again.

I'm jealous. I wish we could afford to travel. I miss it. I miss my mother and brother. I miss the European views, the snowy cities, and the cold weather. Mostly, I miss our family, and how we grew up together in Bucharest.

I have some good news to share. Yossi decided to marry his high school sweetheart, a charming girl, without a doubt. In fact, she and her family, just like us, are originally from Bucharest. She's a teacher.

Kissing and hugging,
Golda

Geneva, Switzerland, October 1967

My dear Golda,

I'm afraid I have some bad news. About a week ago, my Mircea collapsed in the middle of the library. An ambulance rushed him to the hospital.

We're so lucky to have found our place in Switzerland. The hospitals here are modern and well equipped with advanced machines, the best doctors, and progressive treatments, but the news is not good. He has heart disease. Who would believe that? The great big heart, the giving and loving heart of my Mircea threatens to eliminate his existence? And what will happen to me? How will I live without my angel?

Please dear Golda, pray for us.

Friddie

***

Haifa, Israel, October 1969

My Friddie,

I'm a grandmother! My dear Yossi and Hadass gave birth to a beautiful baby girl last week. They called her Michal.

I feel so honored to be able to see my own granddaughter. I'm fortunate to see the next generation.

Yours,

Golda

***

Geneva, Switzerland, October 1970

Dear Golda,

My Mircea decided that it was finally the right time for him to retire. Yesterday, we held a big party at the library and invited all the staff and readers to celebrate with us. The cake was delicious. I was worried that his big gracious heart would not stand the excitement, but my husband's warm and loving eyes calmed my fears.

We rented a small château in Cannes, and we plan to split our time between Geneva and the French Riviera. Now it's finally our time to take things slower.

I miss you,
Friddie

***

Haifa, Israel, April 1971

Dear Friddie,

I'm so excited! My heart is expanding and about to explode! My Yossi, my talented son, was invited to a business meeting, and you will never guess where? Yes, Romania! The country that vomited us out now invites my son to share his wonderful ideas for the development of their seaport.

And my Yossi, my sensitive child, wants to visit his grandmother Rosa. Can you believe it? I can only imagine the exciting meeting between the beloved grandson and his grandmother.

If only I could be there with them.

Please give my love to Mircea.

Yours,
Golda

***

Geneva, Switzerland, January 1972

My dear Golda,

I'm so sorry to hear about your mother's passing.

My heart is broken. My beloved Tanti Rosa has left us. I miss her dearly. The tears keep running down my cheeks.

I'm glad Yossi got to say goodbye to her.

I'm hugging and kissing you.

Friddie

***

Haifa, Israel, July 3, 1972

Telegram

We are sorry to announce the passing of Mr. Aharon (Aurel) Rosenthal, born in Bucharest, Romania, 1904.

The grieving family

***

Geneva, Switzerland, July 1972

My dear Golda,

I'm so sorry to hear about your husband's passing. Aharon was an exemplary family man, a devoted father, and a loving and a supportive spouse.

I weep for the world that has lost such a precious man, and only six months after your mother's passing. I know my Tanti Rosa will take good care of him in Heaven.

I'm so sorry for your loss.

Yours,

Friddie and Mircea

***

Haifa, Israel, May 1973

My Friddie,

The tears of mourning for my mother and Aharon were recently replaced by tears of joy for the birth of my second granddaughter. We decided to give her the name Aharona, in memory of her beloved grandfather.

Now, I'll think of them both in the same breath.

I pray that my granddaughters will only know happiness. I pray for them to find great loving, generous, and kind spouses. As we both did.

Hugging you warmly,

Golda

***

Geneva, Switzerland, October 1974

My dear Golda,

Last week, Mircea and I celebrated twenty years of marriage. Can you believe it?

Twenty years of happiness sweeter than honey. Twenty years of true friendship, one that comes from the heart. Twenty years of understanding each other without words. I won. I thank God I was privileged to know this wonderful man.

You see, Golda, the divine beauty is in the small details, in the simple things. We are fortunate.

Yours forever,
Friddie

***

Haifa, Israel, May 1975

My beloved Friddie,

A few days ago, I wrote you a long letter. I write this postcard to thank you for the package you've sent; it has finally arrived after two months. The package with the skirt, scarf and the pants. Everything looks incredible! You always had a good sense of fashion.

My health is no longer at its best. I guess it's part of getting old. Last week, I was hospitalized and had to undergo surgery. I feel better now. I am recovering slowly and patiently. Trying to think only of good things.

Take care of yourself, my dear.

I pray to God that we'll be able to see each other again.

Love, Golda.

***

Gran Canaria, Spain, February 1978

My sweet and beloved Aurica,

My age—that of menopause—is probably playing tricks on me (I'll be fifty-nine in October). Suddenly and purposelessly, I went through a depressive state. I cried constantly, I couldn't sleep, even if I took sleeping pills, and I couldn't concentrate enough to put my thoughts on paper. I took the doctor's advice and spent over a month in Gran Canaria and now I'm getting better. Me, who usually has a great memory, I'd forget everything. Now I have to respond to thirty-two letters and forty postcards. So much writing. But please believe me that, even though I didn't write to you, my heart was and still is with you, next to you. Besides the fact that I worry about you, I miss you, I miss you terribly.

Why must faith be so cruel that you aren't able to come to me and I am too poor to afford the luxury to come to you?

The years go by faster and faster, and our life is rapidly shortening. I pray to God that He'll do wonders, and we'll see each other again. Out of our entire family, I only keep in touch with you, Puyo, Tanti Zilli and Unchi Alexander. They are doing well in their retirement home. I would love to see Yossi and meet his family.

My dear, Mircea and I wish you all the best. May God give you a long life and good health. What can we, some sad human beings, do, other than obey the will of God? Faith and destiny are the ones in charge, and we are too insignificant to be able to oppose them in any way. Sometimes, when I reflect upon my life, I am inclined to believe that happiness is so ephemeral that it's almost utopic. In order to face the hard challenges of life, I debate philosophy with myself and tell myself... Hey, girl... What's meant to be will be... What's written on your forehead will happen, as the old proverb goes.

This is why I am not afraid of anything. I'm not afraid of diseases or enemies. Of nothing. I've come to the point of convincing myself that we are in the hands of destiny.

That's all, my love. God is with you, so be brave; you're not the one deciding, the Almighty is.

Mircea sends his best regards, as well. Please write to me, at least, so the distance will feel shorter.

I love you,
Friddie

***

Haifa, Israel, April 1978

My dear Friddie,

I wanted to wish you and Mircea a happy Passover from the whole Rosenthal family.

Last night, I celebrated Passover with my dear son, my wonderful daughter-in-law, and my two sweet granddaughters. It was a magical evening. I giggled to myself that, even after twenty-seven years in the Land of Israel, I still have a hard time reading in Hebrew. I actually managed to deal quite well with the songs.

Especially during holidays, I feel a mix of sadness and joy. I miss the Passover celebrations we used to have in Romania. Even after twenty-seven years, I have not forgotten the wonderful delicacies of my mother, may she rest in peace.

I'm sending all my love to you and Mircea. Happy holiday greetings, all the way from Israel to Geneva.

Love you,
Golda

Geneva, Switzerland, March 1979

Golda,

Tears suffocate my throat. My heart aches and cries. Late last night, my Mircea passed away.

Mircea, my soulmate, the person who has always been there by my side, is no more.

My heart shatters to pieces and there is no space to heal. Please pray for me.

Friddie

***

Haifa, Israel, December 1981

Dear Tanti Friddie,

My name is Yossi (Gigi), and I am the son of Golda and Aharon Rosenthal from Haifa.

I found your address among the letters and personal belongings that my mom kept by her bedside.

I'm afraid I have bad news.

My beloved mother passed away unexpectedly last night in her sleep. None of us expected it. At least I take comfort in the fact that she didn't suffer.

I read the letters she kept in her drawer, and I know that my mother cherished you deeply. She was so excited to receive a postcard or a letter from you.

Despite the many stories I have heard from my mother, I, unfortunately, cannot

attest that I remember you. I was very young when you were taken from us.

I would love to keep in touch and hopefully someday we can meet again.

Fondly,
Gigi

***

Cannes, French Riviera, January 1982

My dearest Gigi,

My heart aches at the news that my beloved cousin Golda is gone. There are no words that can comfort and express how great my love and respect were for your mother.

Thank you for attaching a picture of your lovely family, Gigi. I keep all the pictures your mother sent me over the years by my bedside.

After my Mircea passed away, I could no longer stay in our apartment in Geneva, surrounded by memories and longings. A good friend of mine, Edith Blanchett, moved to Cannes on the French Riviera and I moved in with her. I brought my six cats with me and even adopted another local cat here. I'm in good company here. I don't feel lonely.

Edith is here by my side. I like Edith's friendship and the soulful conversations with her remind me of the similar friendship I found with your mother.

Edith also agreed to take care of and adopt all my cats, that are like children to me, when I die. I have left her my modest property in my will.

I'm not afraid of dying, my child. I do not fear it. I am comforted that, up there, at the gates of Heaven, my family and my Mircea will be waiting for me.

Take care of yourself and your family.

Yours,
Friddie

***

Edith Blanchett, Cannes, December 1983

Dear Gigi,

I'm sorry to inform you that Mrs. Fridda Stoleru-Choiboteru passed away last night at home. She was laid to rest and buried this morning in the local cemetery.

The doctor determined that the cause of death was heart fatigue.

I know you're her last remaining relative. Friddie was as precious to me as a sister.

I'm so sorry for our loss.

Edith Blanchett

Epilogue
by the author

In the summer of 2009, my parents came to visit me in my new home in Maryland, on the east coast of the United States, where I had moved with my family and two children four years earlier.

I will never forget that morning when my father and I sat in a local cafe. We relished the caressing rays of the sun. "Daddy," I asked, "tell me Friddie's story again."

And he did.

In December 2009, on the first evening of Hanukkah, my father, Yossi Rosenthal, passed away. An aneurysm cut through his heart.

This is not the place to tell how much my sister and I adored our dad all his life. Nor is it the place to tell how much his death has shattered our hearts and how much his absence is felt every day and in every breath we take.

Dad rarely talked about the hardships he experienced as a child. He came to Israel without knowing the language and lived with his parents in the transit camp at Kfar Hasidim. He never told us how, when he was only a fourteen-year-old, he found work as a messenger boy at the Port of Haifa, riding his bicycle. Or the modest salary he received by the end of each week, which he proudly passed on to his parents to help support the family's needs.

When he turned eighteen years old, as required by the state of Israel, my dad joined the Israeli army. He was proud of his combat service in the Armored Corps, but refrained from telling us about the many friends he lost, and about his hearing that was weakened in a training accident when a missile exploded not far from him. He never complained or grieved. He learned to hide his disappointment and be proud of his accomplishments.

We heard all these stories from our mom.

Mom and Dad's love story began at the All Israel Friends-Alliance high school in Haifa. Mom was in ninth grade and Dad, who was three years older than her, tutored her in math. She helped him with language studies. What a shock it was when the families finally met to plan their children's wedding ceremony, and Eva-Sophia and Golda fell into each other's arms, having met years earlier on the boat to Israel.

Dad never celebrated birthdays. He believed that celebrations were meant to rejoice in successes or accomplishments, and on a person's birthday, he was simply born.

Dad believed in the values of honesty, modesty, and wisdom. There was no one more modest and honest than my father. Even when he already had a secure job, he wanted nothing more than a two-bedroom apartment in Haifa, a used car, and a vacation once a year, no more.

Dad believed in hard work and loyalty to the workplace. After graduating with honors in economics, he returned to his initial job at the Port of Haifa. The same boss who employed him as a fourteen-year-old delivery boy, offered him his first job as an economist. Dad later graduated with a master's degree in economics and business administration from the Technion and progressed to the position of head of the port's economics department.

As long as the port prospered and succeeded, Dad was happy. It was his first love, he would say. The port was there before he even knew Mom, though they had met first on the ship from Constanța. When my sister was born, my father was busy preparing the port's annual budget report. It was Mom who threatened that if he didn't come to the delivery room immediately, she would call her daughter "Budget." The threat worked, and Michal was born.

Dad never stopped studying. Evening courses and professional training became a second career for him. He found himself in language courses, computer programming, mediation management in the workplace, etc. When Dad turned fifty, he decided it was time for a doctorate degree. He graduated three years later and wrote an international research paper on "Free Port Trades." The work was acclaimed, and he became famous as a leader in his field.

Toward the end of his career, Dad was offered a position as the head of the port. He declined the offer. Instead, he decided it was time to give the port the representation it deserved and asked to be appointed as the Haifa Port's spokesman and public relations director. The appointment was given to him immediately.

At age sixty-seven, as required by law, he finally retired. But two months later, he was asked to return to his work. Dad, of course, agreed. At the same time, he was asked to join the Haifa Labor Court and fight for employee justice. He stood by the workers, researching the relevant rulings, day and night. He became the public representative for labor matters.

Dad was a devoted son to his parents. When his father, Aharon, fell ill with cancer, he treated him with dedication and stayed by his side in the hospital until he took his last breath. He also made sure to visit his mother every day and bring her all the groceries from the supermarket. On his parents' grave, he had these words engraved: "To my parents, the precious ones. The unforgettable."

In the summer of 1982, about a year after the death of my grandmother Golda, a guest came for a short visit to my parents' house. The guest was Friddie. My father was ecstatic about her visit. A week earlier, Friddie had decided to take a trip to Israel. Though the trip was rushed, my father quickly got everything together so that she could stay with us. When she arrived, they embraced for a long time.

"Gigi, Gigi," Friddie sobbed on his shoulder. "Finally, we meet again, Gigi."

Friddie stayed with us for six days. I didn't understand their conversations, as they were all in Romanian, a language which I do not speak. Friddie and I would just watch each other, and she would smile, spinning the ring on her finger repeatedly.

One night, I woke up in a panic. I heard someone screaming from the other room. I rushed out and hid in the doorway. My mother and father ran into the guest room. I sneaked over and peered through the door, watching them try to calm her. My mother stroked Friddie's hair, while my dad gave her a glass of water. She shakily drank it, gulping down her pills. We all stayed up with her until she went back to sleep, her soft snores echoing through the house.

During her visit, she told my parents about Mircea's death. His heart disease was raging inside him, his body weak. Friddie called an ambulance, which brought Mircea to a hospital in Geneva.

While he was still conscious in his hospital bed, Mircea had one last request. "After my death," he told Friddie, "please contact King Mihai. Please tell him I didn't forget him. Please tell him how much I loved him, that he was like a brother to me. I forgive him now. I'm confident that, had he known my fate, he would never have asked them to soften my sentence and to send me to the labor camps at the Danube canal. It was an innocent mistake, I'm sure."

I was only nine years old when Friddie came to visit us in Haifa, so I don't remember much. I remember an elderly woman with a smiling face. I remember long, charcoal-black hair with white streaks. I remember a strong smell of dark red nail polish, which was applied often over broken fingernails. I remember scarred hands shoved quickly into white gloves, and a rolling laugh that infected us all. And I remember a family dinner of her favorite Romanian dishes. The joy in her eyes was unforgettable.

Friddie passed away a few months after her visit. I never saw her again.

About a year after my grandmother Golda's death, my father learned of a man named Reuben Sofer, who had emigrated from Romania to Israel. He was a first cousin to my great-grandfather, Reuben Sofer-Isopovichi, who had married Grandmother Rosa. My father believed that this Reuben had the key to the family mystery. Could it be that Reuben's grave was never found? His mother, Golda, had also heard a family rumor that her father, Reuben, had recovered from his coma, remarried, but forgot all about his past. Could it be?

My father posted an ad in the local newspapers and reached out to the national radio station on a special broadcast called "Searching for Relatives," in an attempt to contact Reuben Sofer's family. Unfortunately, all of my father's attempts were unsuccessful. When my father passed away, he still had no information about his grandfather.

I, too, at the time of writing this book, am trying to follow my dad's footsteps and locate the Sofer family. I'm happy to report that, with the help of social media, Facebook groups, and incredibly helpful people, I was able to connect with them. I spoke with two of Reuben Sofer's grandchildren. Unfortunately, at the time of writing this book, no one knows about my great-grandfather Reuben Sofer-Isopovichi's grave or whether he recovered. This family mystery will remain forever unsolved.

Another happy update; while writing the final lines of this book, I was able to connect with Feiga's family members, still living in Israel. I was happy to hear from Feiga's granddaughter that Feiga lived a wonderful life in Israel and fulfilled her heart's desires. Feiga passed away in 1964, surrounded by her family and friends.

Friddie's story is told at every family gathering now, to remind us to be grateful. My sister and I are the last ones who met Friddie in person and can tell her story.

Friddie's story is not just the story of the Postelnic-Isopovichi-Stoleru families. Those stories carry greater messages for all of us. We must learn from history. We must give voice to and tell the stories of those who have been silenced. We must tell, explore, and reveal the truth. No more hiding. No more living in fear.

I chose to write this book and uncover our family story, to let future generations learn from our ancestors' pain.

Although "*we are not required to complete the work*,"[31] we must take the first steps to start it. It is upon us, the descendants of the survivors, those who lived through massacres and death camps, the Holocaust and genocide, to tell their stories. Only we can bring to the public's attention the experiences of our family. We must tell the stories of both those who survived, and those who perished in the cruelty of oppression. We are the keepers, and we must continue telling, or the stories could be lost.

A few years after the death camps of the Danube Canal were closed and the remaining inmates were transferred or released, the green grass grew again. It spread across the land, covering the construction sites and the lonely tombs of the dead. The Danube River has become a fertile paddock for transporting goods, and a hub for tourist boating.

The vast meadows and trees now flourish and bloom. There, above mounds of dirt, among walls of stones, standing tall and proud, glowing in its strength, grows a purple flower. Even places that have seen so much human suffering can become fertile again, where lilac flowers can bloom once again.

— The End —

31 Pirkei Avot 2:16

Acknowledgments

Before my father passed away in 2009, he left behind an old photo album, a partial family tree, and stories that were passed down in my family, from one generation to another. In order to write this book and put together this family puzzle, I needed a lot of help.

I'd like to take this opportunity to thank all the wonderful people who helped, wrote, supported, and shared their stories with me about living in Romania during those years.

Thank you to the Sofer family (the grandchildren of Reuben Sofer, the cousin of my grandmother's missing father); to the Yehezkel family (Feiga's granddaughter), thank you so much for sharing your memories with me. Irina (Adrian's daughter, my grandmother's brother), thank you for the time and patience and for sharing your memories of our extended family and of Grandma Rosa.

To the incredibly helpful people in the Facebook groups (Shorashim, JewishGen, etc.), who helped me post, repost, and share the old photos that finally helped me reconnect with my lost extended family.

A special thanks to Sorin within the Jewish Genealogy in Romanian Moldova Facebook group. Sorin and the group members helped me add more pieces to the family puzzle and locate my Romanian family certificates.

Beno, I highly appreciate all your help and the wisdom you brought into this book. You helped me learn and understand life in

Romania, as if I had lived there myself. By sharing your life stories with me, you made it feel so real. Thank you for corresponding with the archives in Romania and thank you for translating their responses.

I would like to express my gratitude to a large number of people who saw me through this book; to all those who provided support, read, wrote, offered comments, allowed me to quote their remarks, and shared their insight, wisdom, and creativity with me.

This book couldn't have been completed without the talent and the devotion of excellent editors, Hannah Bercovici and Annie Percik. Hannah and Annie dedicated their minds and souls into shaping this story and bringing it to life.

I'd like to extend my appreciation to my beta readers who shared their insights, questions, comments and suggestions with me. I'd like to thank many professionals who assisted in proofreading and designing.

#

Last, but not least: I'm grateful for the support of my family and closest friends.

Mom, you are the role model in my life. You bring so much devotion to our family and ongoing patience to all of us. I could not have written this book without you. Your life experience growing up in Romania, your knowledge of the Romanian language and its history, and the number of hours you dedicated to reading, researching, editing, and translating this book are so much appreciated. I love you!

To my sister, Miki, who helped me research and find the family connections, who cried with me and got excited when we were able to put another puzzle piece in place. To my nieces and nephews,

Gal, Noy, Yam, and Jen, thank you for always supporting me on my journey.

To my children, whose ongoing love and support are more than I could have ever asked for. Shachar and Kiki—you are my inspiration; you make my world complete.

A special thanks to Shoko and Krembo.

Finally, to you, Kobi, my life partner, who supported me through the process, tolerated the huge number of books, diaries, and studies that piled up next to the bed, and understood my frustrations, as well as celebrating my successes. Thank you for being there for me.

I beg forgiveness of all those who have been with me over the course of the years and whose names I have failed to mention.

P.S. I keep posting more photos and family stories on Friddie's Facebook page. Please follow me:

https://www.facebook.com/FriddieStoleru

Resources:

Captivating History. (2021). Romanian history: A captivating guide to the history of Romania and Vlad the Impaler.

Cârja Ion. (1993). Canalul morţii. Cartea Românească, Bucharest.

Cioroianu, A. (2005). *Pe umerii lui Marx. O introducere în istoria comunismului românesc ("On the Shoulders of Marx. An Incursion into the History of Romanian Communism").* Editura Curtea Veche. http://ajcarchives.org/AJC_DATA/Files/1954_10_EastEurope.pdf

Chiru, M., & Gherghina, S. (2010). Promoting Ideology through Social Engineering Experiments: The Danube Black Sea Canal. Transylvanian Review, No. 5

file:///C:/Users/roni3/Downloads/PromotingideologythroughsocialengineeringexperimentstheDanubeBlackSeaCanal.pdf

Promotingideologythroughsocialengineeringexperimentsthe DanubeBlackSeaCanal.pdf

Courtois S., &Kramer, M. (2004). The Black Book of Communism: Crimes, Terror, Repression. Harvard University Press.

Hitchins, K. (2015). A concise history of Romania. Cambridge University Press

Familypedia. (n.d.). *Danube-Black Sea Canal labor camps | Familypedia | Fandom.* Familypedia. Retrieved April 28, 2022, from https://familypedia.fandom.com/wiki/Danube-Black_Sea_Canal_labor_camps#cite_note-graff-12

Manea, G. S. (2014). The Romanian Gulag and its characters. Historical Yearbook, XI-XII, 225–237, from: file:///C:/Users/roni3/Downloads/The_Romanian_Gulag_and_its_Characters_Ca.pdf

9AM News. (2006, March 11). *Procesul Canalului Mortii*. 9AM News. Retrieved April 28, 2022, from https://www.9am.ro/stiri-revista-presei/2006-03-11/procesul-canalului-mortii.html

Petrinca, R. (2017). Halfway between memory and history: Romanian gulag memoirs as a genre. Slovo, 29(1). https://doi.org/10.14324/111.0954-6839.056
https://discovery.ucl.ac.uk/id/eprint/1538686/1/2.pdf

Richard, A. (2021, August 7). One worker on the Danube-Black Sea Canal. Richard Pennington. Retrieved July 6, 2022, from https://richardpennington.com/2021/08/one-worker-on-the-danube-black-sea-canal/

SemiColonWeb. (n.d.). Romania's history. ROMANIA History. Timeline and major Romania historical events. Retrieved July 6, 2022, from https://romaniatourism.com/history.html

Socor, V. (1984, August 31). *The Danube – Black Sea Canal: A Graveyard Revisited*. OSA CEU. http://files.osa.ceu.hu/holdings/300/8/3/text/53-6-1.shtml

Spulber, N. (1954). The Danube – Black Sea Canal and the Russian Control over the Danube. *Economic Geography*, 30(3), 236-245.

Made in United States
Orlando, FL
02 October 2023